PHILIP'S

COLOUR
STAR ATLAS

EPOCH 2000

First published in 1991 by George Philip Limited,
an imprint of Reed Books, Michelin House,
81 Fulham Road, London SW3 6RB,
and Auckland, Melbourne, Singapore and Toronto

ISBN 0–540–06316–9

Design Peter Burt
Page design Louise Dick
Edited by John Woodruff

Typeset by Keyspools Ltd, Golborne, Lancashire

Printed in Hong Kong

Acknowledgements

The authors would like to thank Stephen Adamson, Matthew Butters, Kevin D'Eça, Dr Dorrit Hoffleit, Siān Morgan, Paul Murdin, Dr Jack Sulentic, Dr Wayne Warren Jr, Paul Whittle, and John Woodruff for their help and advice. They would also like to thank the Library of the Institute of Astronomy at the University of Cambridge, the Library of the Royal Astronomical Society, the Royal Greenwich Observatory, the Royal Observatory, Edinburgh, and (NASA) World Data Center-A. Responsibility for errors remains with the authors.

Reference Sources

C. W. Allen, *Astrophysical Quantities*, Athlone Press, 1963.

Richard Hinckley Allen, *Star Names, Their Lore and Meaning*, Dover Publications, 1963.

W. Gliese, *Catalogue of Nearby Stars*, Verlag G. Braun, Karlsruhe, 1969.

Alan Hirshfeld and Roger W. Sinnott (editors), *Sky Catalogue 2000.0*, Cambridge University Press/Sky Publishing Corporation, 1982 (Vol. 1), 1985 (Vol. 2).

Dorrit Hoffleit, Carlos Jaschek and Wayne Warren Jr (editors), *The Bright Star Catalogue*, 5th Edition (Machine Readable), Department of Astronomy, Yale University, distributed NASA 1991.

Dorrit Hoffleit, Michael Saladyga, and Peter Wlasuk (editors), *A Supplement to the Bright Star Catalogue*, Yale University Observatory, 1983.

David H. Hubel, *Eye, Brain, and Vision*, Scientific American Library, 1988.

Valerie Illingworth, *Macmillan Dictionary of Astronomy*, second edition, Macmillan Press, London, 1985.

James B. Kaler, *Stars and Their Spectra*, Cambridge University Press, 1989.

P. N. Kholopov (editor), *General Catalogue of Variable Stars*, fourth edition, Nauka Publishing House, Moscow, 1985.

David Malin and Paul Murdin, *Colours of the Stars*, Cambridge University Press, 1984.

M. Minnaert, *The Nature of Light and Color in the Open Air*, Dover Publications, 1954.

Ian Ridpath (editor), *Norton's 2000.0*, Longman Scientific and Technical/John Wiley & Sons, 1989.

K. Schaifers and H. H. Voigt, *Numerical Data and Functional Relationships in Science and Technology*, Landolt-Börnstein, Group VI, Vol. 2, Springer-Verlag, 1981.

Roger W. Sinnott (editor), *NGC 2000.0*, Cambridge University Press/Sky Publishing Corporation, 1988.

Jack W. Sulentic and William G. Tifft (editors), *Revised New General Catalogue of Non-Stellar Objects*, University of Arizona Press, 1973.

Wil Tirion, *Sky Atlas 2000.0*, Cambridge University Press/Sky Publishing Corporation, 1981.

COLOUR STAR ATLAS

EPOCH 2000

John Cox & Richard Monkhouse

CONTENTS

Opposite page **Part of the Milky Way on the borders of the constellations Sagittarius, Scutum and Serpens**

Near the centre is the Omega or Horseshoe Nebula (M17), with the Eagle Nebula (M18) above it, both giant gas clouds glowing red with the light of ionized hydrogen. Below and to the right lies the Small Sagittarius Star Cloud. It appears blue, probably because there is little obscuring interstellar dust to redden its light, but possibly also because the stars it contains are young and blue.

Colour in Stars

Only a few of the brightest and most strongly coloured stars appear anything other than white to the naked eye. The red stars Antares and Betelgeuse are perhaps the most famous examples; orange–red Aldebaran (the eye of the Bull) and what Ptolemy called 'golden red Arcturus' are further examples of stars whose colour has been recognized from the earliest times. The blue colour of stars such as Regulus and Spica is also easy to see, although the way the eye works in dark conditions means that blue stars do not stand out in quite such an obvious way.

The main reason why stars are differently coloured is that some are hotter than others. Deep in their interior all stars are enormously hot (measured in tens and hundreds of millions of degrees), but their temperature lessens towards their outer layers, and the coolest stars put out most of their visible radiation in the red part of the spectrum, which is why they appear red. Hotter stars (such as our Sun) appear yellow, still hotter stars appear white, and the hottest of all appear blue.

Stars are also differently coloured because the light of some is reddened. Here on Earth the Sun is seen to grow redder as it sets, an effect produced by refraction and absorption in the atmosphere, and accentuated by airborne dust. The reddening of stars is produced by interstellar dust and gas. Most interstellar dust is found in the plane of our Galaxy, so the nearer a star is to the Milky Way, and the more distant it is, the more strongly its light is reddened.

This atlas is concerned with spectral types (the inexperienced observer is recommended to use it alongside a more general atlas or chart). The spectral type of a star is not the same thing as its intrinsic colour, although the two are closely related. When sunlight passes through a triangular glass prism it is split into the colours of the rainbow – a spectrum. The same thing can be done with light from any other star, and almost all the spectra that result can be assigned to one of seven main types. A great deal about the nature of a star can be inferred from its spectrum: how bright it is, how massive it is, whether it is a compact main sequence star or a swollen giant, and, broadly speaking, how old it is and what is happening to it.

With the possible exception of the orange–red stars, the colours that are used to distinguish the spectral types in this atlas entirely overstate the differences in colour that can be seen by eye. They also relate to the intrinsic colour of the star rather than the apparent colour, although for the brighter and (in general) the nearer stars, the intrinsic colour and the apparent colour are likely to be much the same. That most stars do not appear strongly coloured is more to do with the way the eye works than with lack of colour in the stars themselves. However, the perception of star colour improves with practice, and with a pair of binoculars it is possible to gauge the spectral type of most of the brighter stars by eye. In the text that follows, spectral type is considered in several ways: how it is determined, what it says about the nature of the star, and how it relates to the colour seen by eye.

Magnitudes and Units

Apparent Magnitude

The *apparent visual magnitude* (symbol m_v) of a star, or of any other astronomical object, is a measure of how bright it appears to an observer. The ancient Greeks distinguished six kinds of star: the brightest were called 'stars of the first magnitude', those that were not so bright were called 'stars of the second magnitude', and so on down to the dimmest stars that could be seen, 'stars of the sixth magnitude'. This system is still in use, but in a refined and extended way. The modern scale runs through zero and into negative numbers to accommodate particularly bright objects such as Sirius, m_v −1·46. A difference of five magnitudes is equivalent to a factor of a hundred in brightness, so that a star of m_v +1·0 appears to be a hundred times as bright as a star of m_v +6·0. The limit of naked-eye visibility, in other words the magnitude of the dimmest object that can be seen on a clear, moonless night by someone with good eyesight far away from city lights, is about m_v +6·5.

Absolute Magnitude

How bright a star appears to an observer depends on two things: how bright the star really is, and how far away it is. One star can be thousands of times brighter than another, but hundreds of times farther away, so that the two stars appear equally bright. But a value can be put on the intrinsic brightness of stars, by calculating how bright they would appear to be if they were all observed from the same distance. *Absolute visual magnitude* (symbol M_v) is a measure of what the apparent visual magnitude would be if the object were observed from a distance of 10 parsecs (32·6 light years). The bright star Sirius is 2·6 parsecs distant, and has an apparent magnitude m_v −1·46. The apparently less bright Rigel has an apparent magnitude m_v +0·12, but lies about 280 parsecs away. In reality Rigel (M_v −7·1) is about two-and-a-half thousand times brighter than Sirius (M_v +1·4) at the wavelengths of visible light.

Visual Magnitude

In the terms 'apparent visual magnitude' and 'absolute visual magnitude', the word 'visual' is used in a special sense: it signifies that the intensity of light has been measured at the specific wavelength of 550 nanometres (see below). This wavelength corresponds to the peak sensitivity at the centre of the human eye. The eye is sensitive to light only within the band 390–760 nm; this is the *visible spectrum*, 'visible' in the sense that the human eye can see it.

Nanometres and Angstroms

The *nanometre* (symbol nm, one thousand millionth of a metre, or 10^{-9}m) is the preferred unit of wavelength for scientists concerned with the human eye, but in some contexts astronomers use the smaller *angstrom* unit (symbol Å). There are 10 angstroms to the nanometre (1 nm = 10 Å), so that a wavelength of 550 nm is the same as a wavelength of 5,500 Å. In astronomy the angstrom is gradually giving way to the nanometre.

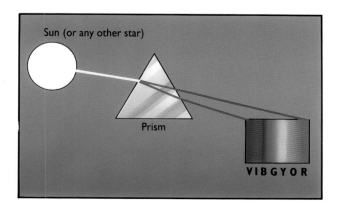

Figure 1   White Light Split by a Prism to Form a Spectrum

Frequency (hertz)		Wavelength (metres)	
10^{23}	Cosmic rays (principally atomic nuclei)	3×10^{-15}	
10^{22}	γ-rays	3×10^{-14}	
10^{21}	γ-rays, X-rays	3×10^{-13}	
10^{20}	X-rays	3×10^{-12}	
10^{19}	X-rays	3×10^{-11}	
10^{18}	'soft' X-rays, ultraviolet (UV)	3×10^{-10}	3 Å
10^{17}	Ultraviolet	3×10^{-9}	3 nm
10^{16}	Ultraviolet	3×10^{-8}	
10^{15}	Visible light (390–760 nm)	3×10^{-7}	300 nm
10^{14}	Infrared (IR)	3×10^{-6}	3 μm
10^{13}	Infrared	3×10^{-5}	
10^{12}	Far infrared	3×10^{-4}	
10^{11}		3×10^{-3}	3 mm
10^{10}	Radar	3×10^{-2}	3 cm
1 GHz 10^{9}	Microwave, radio, 'cellular' communications	3×10^{-1}	
10^{8}	Television and VHF FM radio	3	3 m
10^{7}	Short-wave radio (AM)	3×10	
1 MHz 10^{6}	Medium-wave radio (AM)	3×10^{2}	
10^{5}	Long-wave radio	3×10^{3}	3 km
10^{4}	Very long wave radio (military submarine communications)	3×10^{4}	
1 kHz 10^{3}		3×10^{5}	
10^{2}		3×10^{6}	
10^{1}	AC mains supply	3×10^{7}	
1 Hz 1		3×10^{8}	

Figure 2   The Electromagnetic Spectrum

The Electromagnetic Spectrum

The most familiar form of electromagnetic radiation is visible light. 'White' light, such as sunlight, is a mixture of light at different wavelengths. On passing through a prism, white light is split into the colours of the rainbow (see Fig. 1). This is a result of refraction, the change in direction of light as it passes from one medium, such as air, into another, such as glass. The extent to which light is refracted depends on its wavelength: light of short wavelengths (blue) is refracted more strongly than light of long wavelengths (red). There are seven colours that are traditionally identified in a spectrum: red, orange, yellow, green, blue, indigo, and violet.

The human eye is sensitive to electromagnetic radiation only in the narrow band of wavelengths from 390 to 760 nm. Light is not visible outside this range. Most readers will be familiar with the idea of invisible light, the 'black' light of ultraviolet (UV). Also familiar is the infrared (IR) radiation that can be felt near hot surfaces. But the electromagnetic spectrum extends far beyond these familiar if invisible extensions of the purely visible spectrum (see Fig. 2).

Electromagnetic radiation ranges from low frequency, low energy, long wavelength radio waves at one end of the spectrum, to high frequency, high energy, short wavelength γ-rays at the other. Electromagnetic energy is produced by heat: as material is heated the atoms and molecules in it start to collide. Energy lost in these collisions is released as electromagnetic radiation. How much energy is released and at what wavelengths is directly related to the surface temperature of the radiating material.

A cool body radiates most energy in the infrared. The hotter the body becomes, the shorter the wavelength at which most of its energy is emitted. For example, an old-fashioned flat iron heated by the side of a fire will radiate in the infrared, and although the warmth may be felt, the iron will still appear black. If the iron is put in the fire it will get hotter; its surface temperature will rise, and it will start to glow red-hot. It will then be putting out more energy in the infrared than it was before, but its overall energy output will be very much greater, and some of its radiation will be sufficiently energetic to be seen as visible light.

The overall distribution of energy at various wavelengths follows a curve whose peak is related to the temperature of the radiating surface. The mathematically ideal form of this curve is the so-called *blackbody curve* (see Fig. 3), a blackbody being a theoretically perfect radiator, and for that matter absorber, of energy. Stars are not perfect blackbodies, but their underlying energy radiation does fit the blackbody curve fairly well. Cool stars, stars with a radiating surface of around 3,500 degrees kelvin (symbol K, subtract 273 to convert to degrees Celsius), put out most of their energy in the infrared, and their blackbody curve drops away towards the blue end of the visible spectrum. The blackbody curve of a hot star (15,000 K and above) climbs towards the blue end of the spectrum, and peaks in the ultraviolet. A middle to low temperature star such as the Sun (5,800 K) has a radiation peak towards the middle of the visible spectrum, and this can be taken to be one reason why our eyes are sensitive in the range that they are.

The *effective temperature* of a star is its surface temperature, calculated as if it were a blackbody of the same radius as the star, and emitting the same amount of energy.

Wavelength and Photons

The vocabulary of radio, which includes 'wavelengths' and 'wavebands', has made it natural to think of some particular part of the electromagnetic spectrum, such as a beam of light or a radio signal, as a continuous stream of radiation.

Experiments with X-rays and γ-rays led to the discovery that there is a minimum size to the amount of energy that can be measured at a particular wavelength. This minimum size is called a *quantum*, and the inability to measure amounts smaller than one quantum is not a limitation of the measuring equipment, but a sign that the quantum is the basic unit or 'package' of energy, and that additional radiation arrives in further whole-number multiples of this quantity. Electromagnetic energy can accordingly be thought of as being carried in discrete packages, massless subatomic particles called *photons*.

The wave description of electromagnetic radiation is only partly displaced by the quantum description. The usual compromise is to say that electromagnetic radiation has a dual nature: in some contexts its behaviour is best described in terms of waves, in other contexts it is best described in terms of particles. Both ways are used in describing what happens to electromagnetic radiation as it leaves the surface of a star.

The Production of Spectral Lines

Spectral lines are produced by atoms of particular elements (and, in cooler stars, by molecules) in the atmosphere of a star. As radiation passes through, the atmosphere acts as a selective filter, absorbing the radiation at particular wavelengths. This process

Figure 3
Blackbody Curves

A blackbody curve shows the intensity of radiation over the electromagnetic spectrum for a perfect radiator at a given temperature. Stars are not perfect blackbodies, but the curves shown here roughly match the radiation from B, G, and giant K types, which have distinct profiles through the visible spectrum. (The units of the vertical energy scale are arbitrary.)

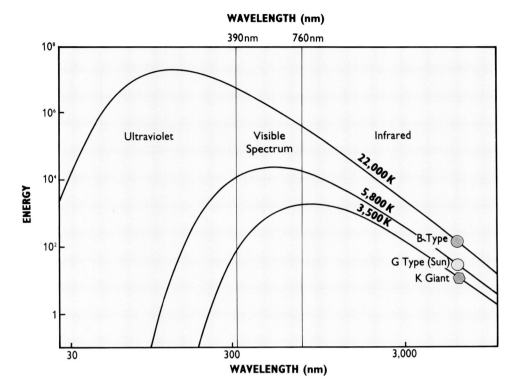

creates shadows, *absorption lines* concentrated at specific wavelengths, and these are the characterizing features of a star's spectrum.

Absorption is explained in terms of the subatomic behaviour of electrons in orbit around a central nucleus. Electrons can orbit only in particular paths; there are no in-between positions. Each path corresponds to a particular energy level in the electron, and the difference in energy between two levels corresponds to a precise amount, an energy quantum. The size of the quantum depends on the nature and condition of the element.

In the photon model of electromagnetic radiation, energy escapes from a star as a stream of discrete particles, photons, each of which carries a precise energy quantum. Higher energy photons are particles of electromagnetic radiation with short wavelengths; lower energy photons are particles with longer wavelengths. As the photons pass through the stellar atmosphere, they move through the atomic fields of its individual atoms. If the energy quantum of a photon passing through an atom precisely matches the quantum that an electron in that atom requires to jump up some particular number of energy levels, then the photon is absorbed, and the electron jumps up. If the energy quantum of the photon is the wrong size, nothing happens, and the photon passes on.

If there is a match, and the electron jumps up, usually it will then immediately make the same jump down again, emitting the same size of photon it absorbed. However, the emitted photon can shoot off in any direction: it is as likely to go straight back into the star as it is to continue its escape. One way absorption lines are formed is by the star's atmosphere acting as a reflection layer, mirroring back energy at particular wavelengths and creating

'shadows' in the radiation that escapes.

A different process produces *emission lines*. An electron is capable of jumping entirely out of its orbit. It does not have to absorb a photon of some particular energy quantum to do this – the photon simply has to have enough energy to free the electron. The free electron swerves around the fields of neighbouring atoms, releasing low energy photons, until sufficient energy has been lost for it to be captured by a nucleus which is itself missing an electron. As it is captured it descends through the energy levels of its new home, emitting quantized photons as it does so. The effect is to split high energy photons of no wavelength in particular into a number of lower energy photons, some of which are quantized at particular wavelengths. This process creates the emission lines found in the spectra of high temperature stars.

An atom or molecule that has lost one or more of its electrons is said to be *ionized*. Physical collisions between atoms also knock electrons out of orbit. The violence and frequency of collision increases with higher temperatures and gas densities. The remaining electrons in an ionized atom produce particularly clear absorption lines; atoms and molecules with more electrons ionize more easily, and the absorption lines produced by ionized elements and molecules are a particularly good indicator of the temperature and pressure of a star's atmosphere (see Table 1).

Spectral Types

To record a stellar spectrum, light from a star is collected in a telescope, passed through a slit, diffracted through a prism or across a diffraction grating, and focused in an arrangement called a *spectrograph*. The

resulting spectrum (sometimes called a *spectrogram*) is seen to contain bars of shadow (absorption lines) and bars of concentrated illumination (emission lines). The classification of stellar spectra began with Joseph von Fraunhofer, who recorded over 500 lines in a solar spectrum taken in 1814. These lines are known today as *Fraunhofer lines*, and some of his notation is still in use (see Fig. 4).

Spectra can vary considerably from one star to another. At first sight, some show only a few lines, while others show dozens; the lines themselves differ, appearing hazy in one spectrum and sharp in another. These distinctions are the basis for sorting spectra, and by extension stars, into a number of *spectral types*.

The *Harvard classification* of spectral types (see Fig. 5) emerged from investigations by Edward C. Pickering and Wilhelmina Fleming in the 1880s and 1890s, and by Antonia Maury and Annie Jump Cannon in the 1890s and 1900s. In its modern form the Harvard system identifies seven major types: O, B, A, F, G, K, and M, each of which is broken down into subtypes: O5, O6, O7, O8, O9·5, B0, B1, B2, and so on. Different positions in the sequence are marked by the appearance, strength, and disappearance of particular lines, and these features are the basis of identification.

At one time it was conjectured that the sequence represented the life of a star, that stars began life as O types and gradually aged through the sequence to end up as M types. This theory turned out to be mistaken, but one consequence is that spectral types are still referred to as *early* and *late*, so that B types are early, and K types are late, and a B0 star is 'earlier' than a B2 star. It is now clear that the Harvard system instead represents a temperature sequence, with O types the hottest and M types the coolest, and the 'earlier' a star is, the hotter it is.

Table 1   Characteristics of the Principal Spectral Types

Type	Line characteristics	Effective temperature (K)
O	He II (ionized helium), emission lines	30,000–50,000
B	He I (neutral helium)	10,000–30,000
A	H (hydrogen)	7,250–10,000
F	Neutral metals*, H	6,000–7,250
G	Neutral metals, Ca II (ionized calcium)	5,000–6,000
K	Ca II, Ca I, molecular lines	3,500–5,000
M	Titanium oxide	2,500–3,500

* In astronomy, unlike chemistry, 'metal' means any element heavier than helium.

Figure 4   Solar Spectrum with Fraunhofer Lines

In 1814 Joseph von Fraunhofer catalogued absorption lines in the solar spectrum. The Fraunhofer lines C to K are produced by absorption in the Sun's atmosphere; lines A and B are superimposed by absorption in the Earth's atmosphere.

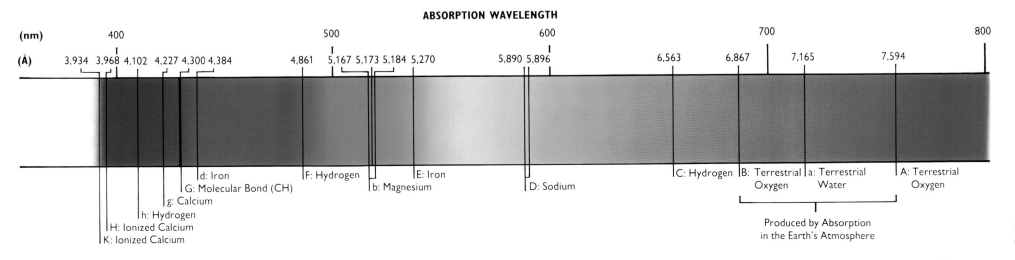

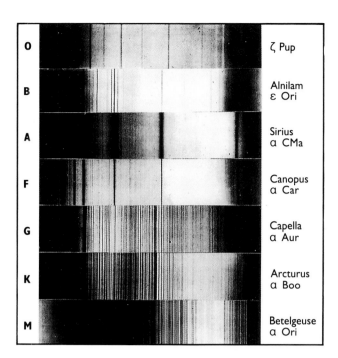

O		ζ Pup
B		Alnilam ε Ori
A		Sirius α CMa
F		Canopus α Car
G		Capella α Aur
K		Arcturus α Boo
M		Betelgeuse α Ori

Figure 5   Harvard Series of Spectra

Spectrograms made in the 1890s, showing the basis for the Harvard OBAFGKM classification. The underlying basis for the classification is a temperature continuum, with stars of each type showing absorptions characteristic of elements at a particular temperature. Emission lines appear in O types; A types show strong hydrogen absorptions at the blue end of the spectrum; K and M types show rich patterns of absorption lines produced by simple molecules. Hot stars show fewer absorption lines than cool stars.

The Hertzsprung–Russell Diagram

Named after its independent discovery in 1911 by Ejnar Hertzsprung and in 1913 by Henry Norris Russell, the *Hertzsprung–Russell diagram* (HR diagram) plots the luminosity of stars along the vertical axis against their spectral class along the horizontal axis (see Fig. 6). Variants of the HR diagram show colour index (see Fig. 14, p. 38) or effective temperature on the horizontal axis, and may represent magnitude as absolute visual magnitude (measured at visible wavelengths) or as *absolute bolometric magnitude* (measured across all wavelengths). This enables different kinds of measurements to be checked against one another, and the HR diagram has become the standard means of correlating the properties of stars.

When Russell plotted the absolute magnitude of nearby stars against spectral class, he discovered that they fell into two groups. Most appeared along a band that crossed the diagram from top left to bottom right, and a more scattered grouping of stars, with intrinsic luminosities hundreds and even thousands of times greater, appeared towards the top of the diagram. If spectral type were indicative of a particular surface temperature, then the more luminous examples could be that way only because their surface area was very much larger.

The spectra of these two groups of stars were subtly different. Those of stars in the upper group had more clearly defined lines, and (ionization) lines found in the lower group were missing. In the 1920s Albert A. Michelson made early measurements of stellar diameters, and confirmed that stars with upper group type spectra were enormously larger than their lower group counterparts. The upper group were given the name *giant stars*, and the lower group *dwarf stars*.

Although giants are very much larger than dwarfs, they do not contain any more material. Indeed, giants

were once dwarfs themselves (see 'Stellar evolution', p. 7). The essential quality of a giant star is that its outer regions are expanded and thinned out. The diameter of a giant star can be 50 times the diameter of a dwarf star of the same mass, making its average density 125,000 times lower.

Luminosity Classes

Giant stars (and, for that matter, dwarf stars) can be of several types. The *MK system*, devised in the 1930s by W. W. Morgan and P. C. Keenan of Yerkes Observatory, extends the Harvard system by ordering stars into a number of *luminosity classes*. The majority of stars are found on what is called the *main sequence*, running from bright blue stars (at the middle left on the HR diagram) to dim red stars (to the lower right). These are the original dwarf stars, luminosity class V.

Stars above the main sequence are assigned to various classes of giants, and stars below the main sequence to specialized categories of dwarfs.

0	Extreme supergiants
Ia	Luminous supergiants
Iab	Supergiants
Ib	Less luminous supergiants
II	Bright giants
III	Giants
IV	Subgiants
V	Dwarfs (main sequence stars)
VI	Subdwarfs
VII	White dwarfs

Particular spectral features are denoted by a system of suffixes; some of the most commonly used are:

e	emission lines
m	metal absorption lines

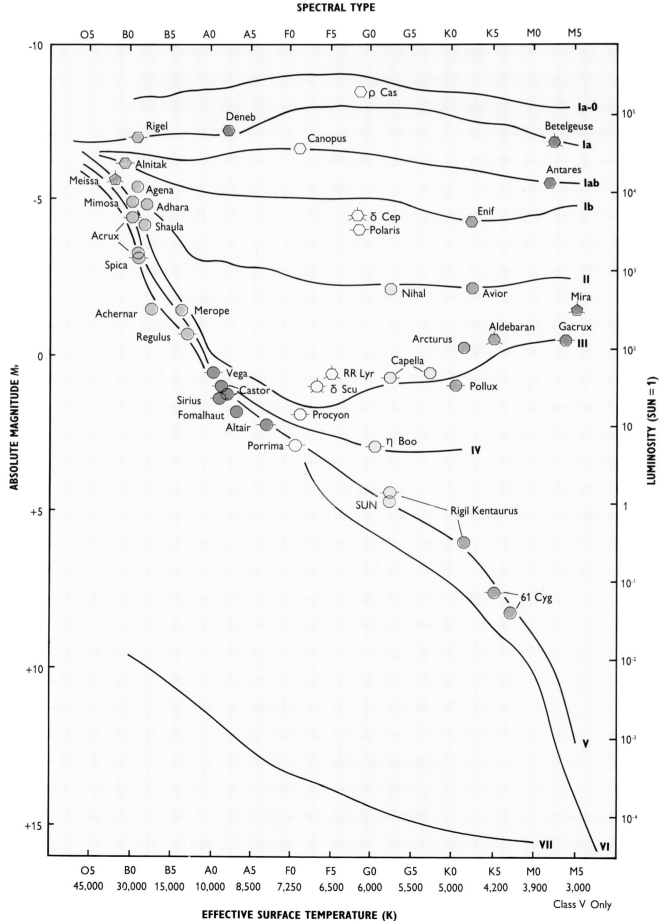

Figure 6   The Hertzsprung–Russell diagram

The Hertzsprung–Russell (HR) diagram is used to plot stellar luminosity against colour, temperature, or spectral type. The luminosity classes shown on the diagram represent an idealization of the way that star positions line up into discrete bands (values after Landolt–Börnstein).

n	diffuse lines (produced by rapid rotation)
p	peculiarity (sometimes follows another, e.g. ep = emission peculiar)
pec.	altogether peculiar (spectrum not properly classifiable)
s	sharp lines
v	variable spectrum

A star's full *spectral classification* consists of a capital letter and arabic numeral to denote its type and subtype, a roman numeral to indicate its luminosity class, and lower case letters to denote special features of its spectrum. For example, Sirius has the classification A1Vm, meaning that it is an A type star of subcategory 1, luminosity class V (a dwarf main sequence star), and its spectrum shows metal absorption lines. Acrux has the classification B0·5IV + B1Vn: it is a binary star (two stars in orbit round a common centre of gravity); the primary member is a B type, subcategory 0·5, luminosity class IV (a subgiant), and the secondary member is a B1 main sequence star with diffuse spectral lines.

Stellar Evolution

Stars are thought to form when a cloud of gas and dust condenses under gravity to form a body of material that is massive enough for nuclear fusion to start at its centre. Starbirth takes place in enormous dust clouds along the plane of the Galaxy, where it is assisted in ways not yet well understood by factors such as pressure and gravity waves, and where the contracting material condenses into a cluster of stars. Open clusters are examples of such groups of 'recently' formed stars, and these are typically found close to the plane of the Milky Way.

As the gas contracts, the atoms start to collide with each other and generate heat. If the body of material is large enough, the temperature reaches 10,000,000 K at the centre of the contracting mass, and the nuclear fusion reaction that converts hydrogen into helium begins. The gravitational attraction of the stellar material (attempting to contract the star further) is checked by the radiation pressure resulting from the reaction (attempting to blow the star up), and the star enters an initial period of instability. T Tauri stars, a type of variable star (see p. 34), are thought to be examples of stars that have recently contracted from surrounding gas clouds.

Bodies of less than 0·08 solar masses (8% of the Sun's mass) do not generate a sufficiently high temperature for nuclear fusion to begin. They may generate enough heat through gravitational contraction to enjoy a brief life as *brown dwarfs*, radiating energy at infrared and radio wavelengths, or, if formed in company with true stars they may become gas planets such as our own Jupiter, Saturn, Uranus, and Neptune, but they will not produce energy by nuclear fusion, and will not therefore be true stars. In the opposite case of a very massive cloud of condensing gas, radiation pressure from the fusion reaction blows away the outlying material before it can coalesce, and there appears to be an upper limit on stellar mass in the region of 100–200 solar masses.

Probably the most massive star identified in the Milky Way Galaxy is η Carinae, believed to be in the region of 120 solar masses. For ten years around 1840 it flared up to m_v −0·8, but shrouded itself in so much dust that it has now faded to m_v +6·2. The dust has also made it impossible to obtain a spectrum, although the star is commonly conjectured to be a supermassive O type.

The Main Sequence

As a newly formed star stabilizes, it drops down the HR diagram and takes up a place on the main sequence. Just where it settles depends on its initial

mass (see Fig. 7). In high mass stars more core material undergoes more complicated fusion reactions than in low mass stars. High mass stars burn hotter, faster, and bluer than low mass stars, which burn cooler, slower, and redder. Stars join the main sequence at a particular position, and stay close to their original position for the whole of their main sequence lifetime.

The initial hydrogen-to-helium reaction at a star's core is the most energetic of all possible reactions, and a star of one solar mass like the Sun has enough core material to keep it quietly in place on the main sequence for around 9,000,000,000 years; in the Sun's case about half this time is believed to have elapsed.

Of the stars shown in this atlas, O types account for 0·5%, B for 19%, A for 22%, F for 14%, G for 13%, K for 25%, and M for 6%. Of the 1,500 stars and star systems listed in Gliese's *Catalogue of Nearby Stars* as lying within 70 light years of the Sun, there are no O types, and only one B type (α Gruis). A types make up approximately 1%, F 10%, G 20%, K 25%, and M types approximately 45%. The majority of stars in the solar neighbourhood are rather smaller than the Sun, typically main sequence M types of around 0·4 solar masses. Such stars are intrinsically very dim (m_v about +10), and none of them is near enough to be seen with the naked eye (all the M types shown on the maps are red giants). The expected main sequence lifetime of M type stars exceeds the elapsed age of the Universe (believed to be about 15,000,000,000 years), so one reason why there are so many of them is that they last a long time.

High mass stars are found at the blue end of the spectrum, and are very rare. They burn up their fuel so quickly that (in astronomical terms) they do not last very long, but because they burn so quickly they are enormously bright and visible over great distances, and thus seem quite numerous. They are concentrated in the plane of the Galaxy because this is where most stars are now formed, and high mass stars do not last long enough to drift away from their birthplace.

The hottest and most massive main sequence stars are O types. These very high mass stars are extremely rare (although they are so luminous that quite a few can be seen – Orion is a good place to look). Their very high core temperatures mean that they quickly switch to more complicated reactions, and their main sequence lifetime is very short.

The fusion of hydrogen into helium releases more energy than any other nuclear reaction, and, with the possible exception of O types, all stars spend most of their active life as main sequence stars burning hydrogen into helium at their core. Stars of less than 0·5 solar masses (main sequence K and M types) are unable to do anything else: they cannot reach a sufficiently high internal temperature for any other sort of reaction, and at some point in the future these stars will run out of core fuel, drop down the HR diagram, and fade away, to white dwarfs and finally to 'black' dwarfs.

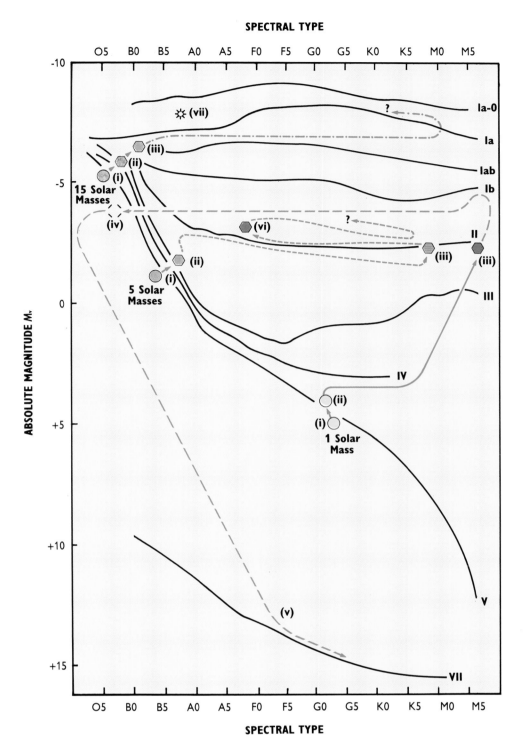

Continued on p. 34

Figure 7 Stellar Evolution on the HR Diagram

Evolutionary pathways are shown here for stars of 1, 5, and 15 solar masses. On the main sequence (i) a star fuses hydrogen into helium in its core. A star spends most of its active life on the main sequence, during which period it brightens slightly. Once the core has exhausted its supply of hydrogen (ii), it contracts and heats up. The star brightens and its outer layers expand, and it moves up and across the diagram, becoming a giant. When the core temperature reaches 100 million degrees kelvin, helium begins fusing into carbon in the core (iii). (Beyond this stage, the evolutionary pathways are somewhat tentative.) A star of less than 1·4 solar masses cannot progress to burning heavier elements. When its core helium is exhausted, the core contracts and the star moves quickly across the diagram and blows off its outer envelope as a planetary nebula (iv). When the inert core stops contracting the star drops down the diagram to fade away as a white dwarf (v), finally becoming a black dwarf. A star of more than 2 solar masses, however, will go on to burn carbon in its core and helium in the surrounding layer. As the balance of reactions shifts, the star executes a series of 'blue loops' (vi) that take it zigzagging up the diagram. Very high mass stars are believed to produce iron-rich cores that eventually collapse, triggering a supernova explosion (vii).

Northern
Key Map

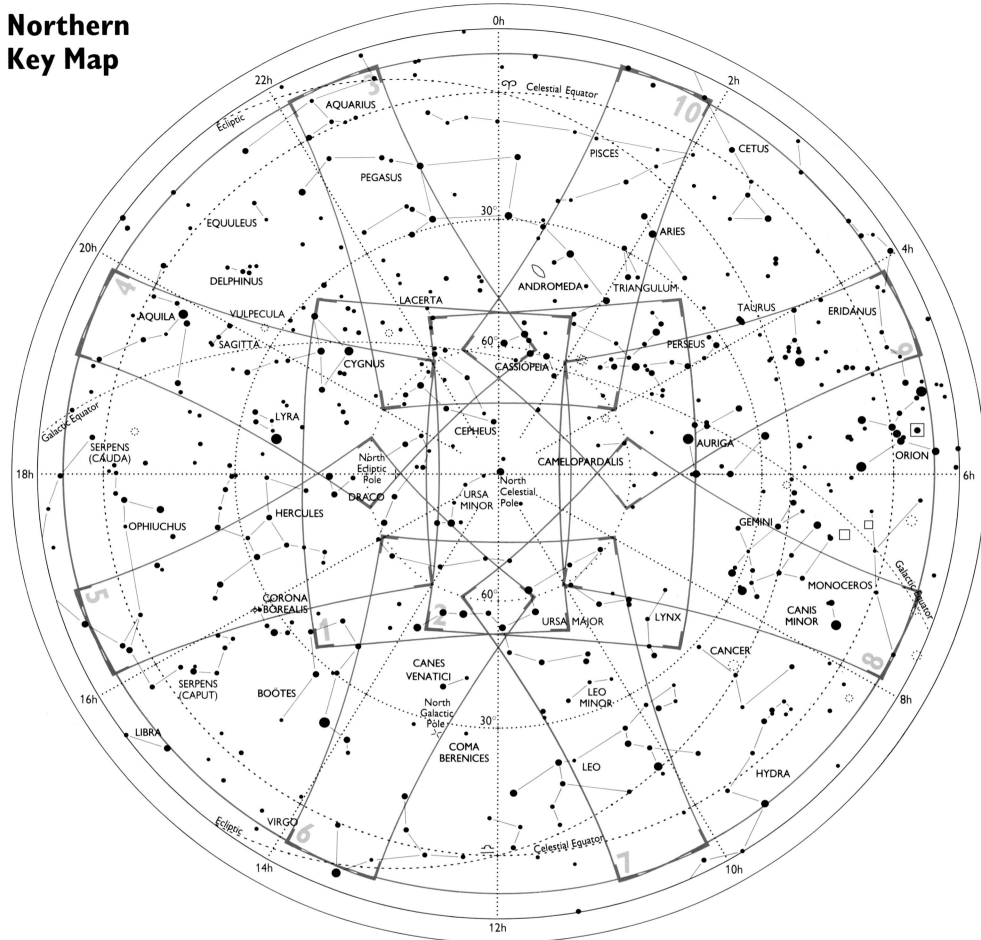

Index of constellations

The genitive forms and three-letter abbreviations are used with individual star designations (see p.35). The map number given for each constellation is the principal one on which the constellation appears.

Constellation	English name	Genitive	Abbreviation	Map	Constellation	English name	Genitive	Abbreviation	Map	Constellation	English name	Genitive	Abbreviation	Map
Andromeda	Andromeda	Andromedae	And	10	Capricornus	The Goat	Capricorni	Cap	11	Cygnus	The Swan	Cygni	Cyg	3
Antlia	The Air Pump	Antliae	Ant	15	Carina	The Keel	Carinae	Car	20	Delphinus	The Dolphin	Delphini	Del	3
Apus	The Bird of Paradise	Apodis	Aps	19	Cassiopeia	Cassiopeia	Cassiopeiae	Cas	2	Dorado	The Goldfish	Dorādus	Dor	20
					Centaurus	The Centaur	Centauri	Cen	14	Draco	The Dragon	Draconis	Dra	1
Aquarius	The Water Carrier	Aquarii	Aqr	11	Cepheus	Cepheus	Cephei	Cep	1	Equuleus	The Little Horse	Equulei	Equ	3
Aquila	The Eagle	Aquilae	Aql	3	Cetus	The Whale	Ceti	Cet	17	Eridanus	The River (Eridanus)	Eridani	Eri	17
Ara	The Altar	Arae	Ara	12	Chamaeleon	The Chameleon	Chamaeleontis	Cha	20					
Aries	The Ram	Arietis	Ari	9	Circinus	The Compasses	Circini	Cir	19	Fornax	The Furnace	Fornacis	For	17
Auriga	The Charioteer	Aurigae	Aur	8	Columba	The Dove	Columbae	Col	16	Gemini	The Twins	Geminorum	Gem	8
Boötes	The Herdsman	Boötis	Boo	5	Coma Berenices	Berenice's Hair	Comae Berenices	Com	6	Grus	The Crane	Gruis	Gru	11
Caelum	The Graving Tool	Caeli	Cae	16	Corona Australis	The Southern Crown	Coronae Australis	CrA	12	Hercules	Hercules	Herculis	Her	4
Camelopardalis	The Giraffe	Camelopardalis	Cam	2	Corona Borealis	The Northern Crown	Coronae Borealis	CrB	5	Horologium	The (Pendulum) Clock	Horologii	Hor	20
Cancer	The Crab	Cancri	Cnc	7						Hydra	The Water Snake (Sea Serpent)	Hydrae	Hya	15
Canes Venatici	The Hunting Dogs	Canum Venaticorum	CVn	6	Corvus	The Crow	Corvi	Crv	14					
Canis Major	The Greater Dog	Canis Majoris	CMa	16	Crater	The Cup	Crateris	Crt	14	Hydrus	The Smaller Water Snake	Hydri	Hyi	20
Canis Minor	The Lesser Dog	Canis Minoris	CMi	7	Crux	The Cross	Crucis	Cru	19					

Southern Key Map

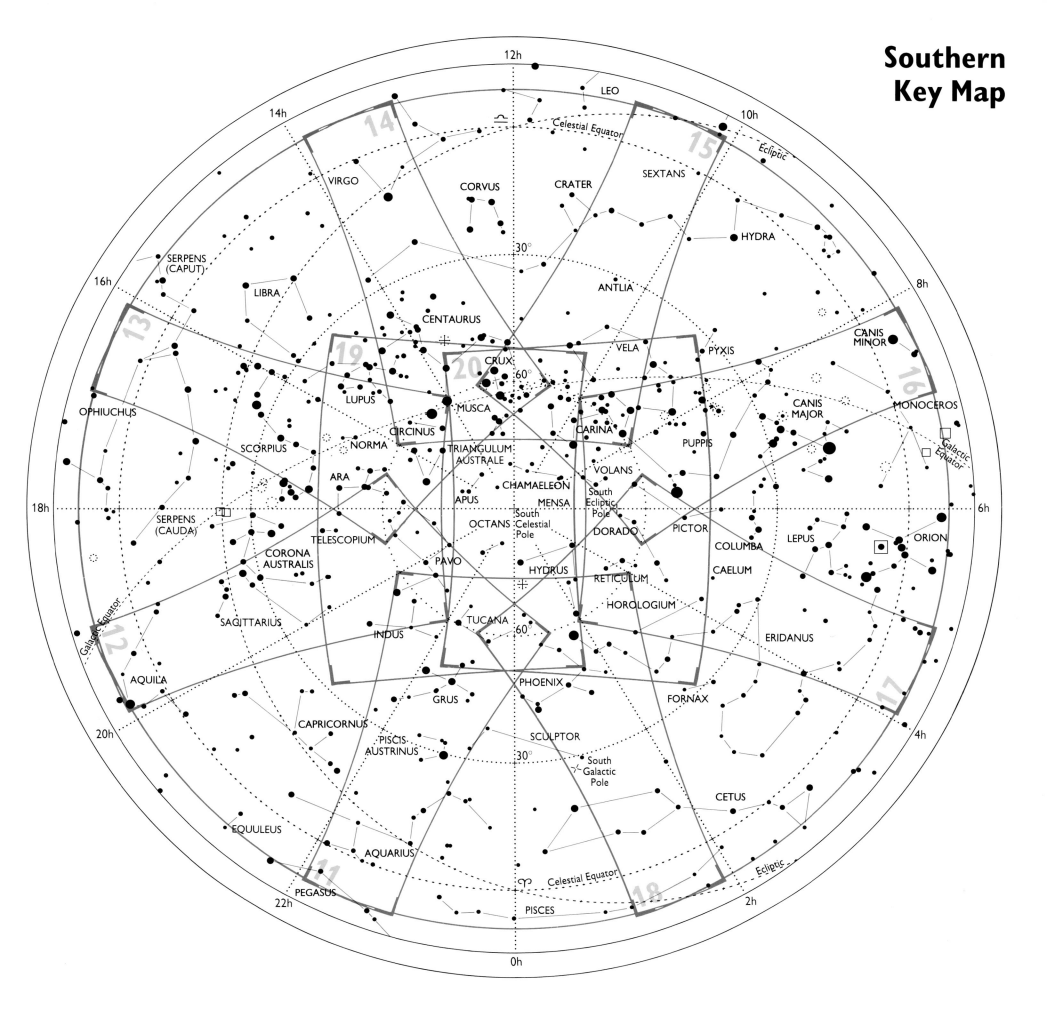

Constellation	English name	Genitive	Abbreviation	Map	Constellation	English name	Genitive	Abbreviation	Map	Constellation	English name	Genitive	Abbreviation	Map
Indus	The Indian	Indi	Ind	19	Orion	Orion	Orionis	Ori	8	Scutum	The Shield	Scuti	Sct	12
Lacerta	The Lizard	Lacertae	Lac	10	Pavo	The Peacock	Pavonis	Pav	19	Serpens	The Serpent	Serpentis	Ser	5/12
Leo	The Lion	Leonis	Leo	6	Pegasus	Pegasus	Pegasi	Peg	10	Sextans	The Sextant	Sextantis	Sex	15
Leo Minor	The Smaller Lion	Leonis Minoris	LMi	7	Perseus	Perseus	Persei	Per	9	Taurus	The Bull	Tauri	Tau	9
Lepus	The Hare	Leporis	Lep	16	Phoenix	The Phoenix	Phoenicis	Phe	18	Telescopium	The Telescope	Telescopii	Tel	12
Libra	The Scales	Librae	Lib	13	Pictor	The Painter	Pictoris	Pic	16	Triangulum	The Triangle	Trianguli	Tri	9
Lupus	The Wolf	Lupi	Lup	13	Pisces	The Fishes	Piscium	Psc	10	Triangulum Australe	The Southern Triangle	Trianguli Australis	TrA	19
Lynx	The Lynx	Lyncis	Lyn	7	Piscis Austrinus	The Southern Fish	Piscis Austrini	PsA	11	Tucana	The Toucan	Tucanae	Tuc	20
Lyra	The Lyre	Lyrae	Lyr	4	Puppis	The Stern	Puppis	Pup	15	Ursa Major	The Great Bear	Ursae Majoris	UMa	6
Mensa	The Table (Mountain)	Mensae	Men	20	Pyxis	The Mariner's Compass	Pyxidis	Pyx	15	Ursa Minor	The Little Bear	Ursae Minoris	UMi	1
Microscopium	The Microscope	Microscopii	Mic	11	Reticulum	The Net	Reticuli	Ret	20	Vela	The Sails	Velorum	Vel	15
Monoceros	The Unicorn	Monocerotis	Mon	16	Sagitta	The Arrow	Sagittae	Sge	3	Virgo	The Virgin	Virginis	Vir	14
Musca	The Fly	Muscae	Mus	19	Sagittarius	The Archer	Sagittarii	Sgr	12	Volans	The Flying Fish	Volantis	Vol	20
Norma	The Level	Normae	Nor	13	Scorpius	The Scorpion	Scorpii	Sco	12	Vulpecula	The Fox	Vulpeculae	Vul	3
Octans	The Octant	Octantis	Oct	19	Sculptor	The Sculptor	Sculptoris	Scl	18					
Ophiuchus	The Serpent-Holder	Ophiuchi	Oph	12										

9

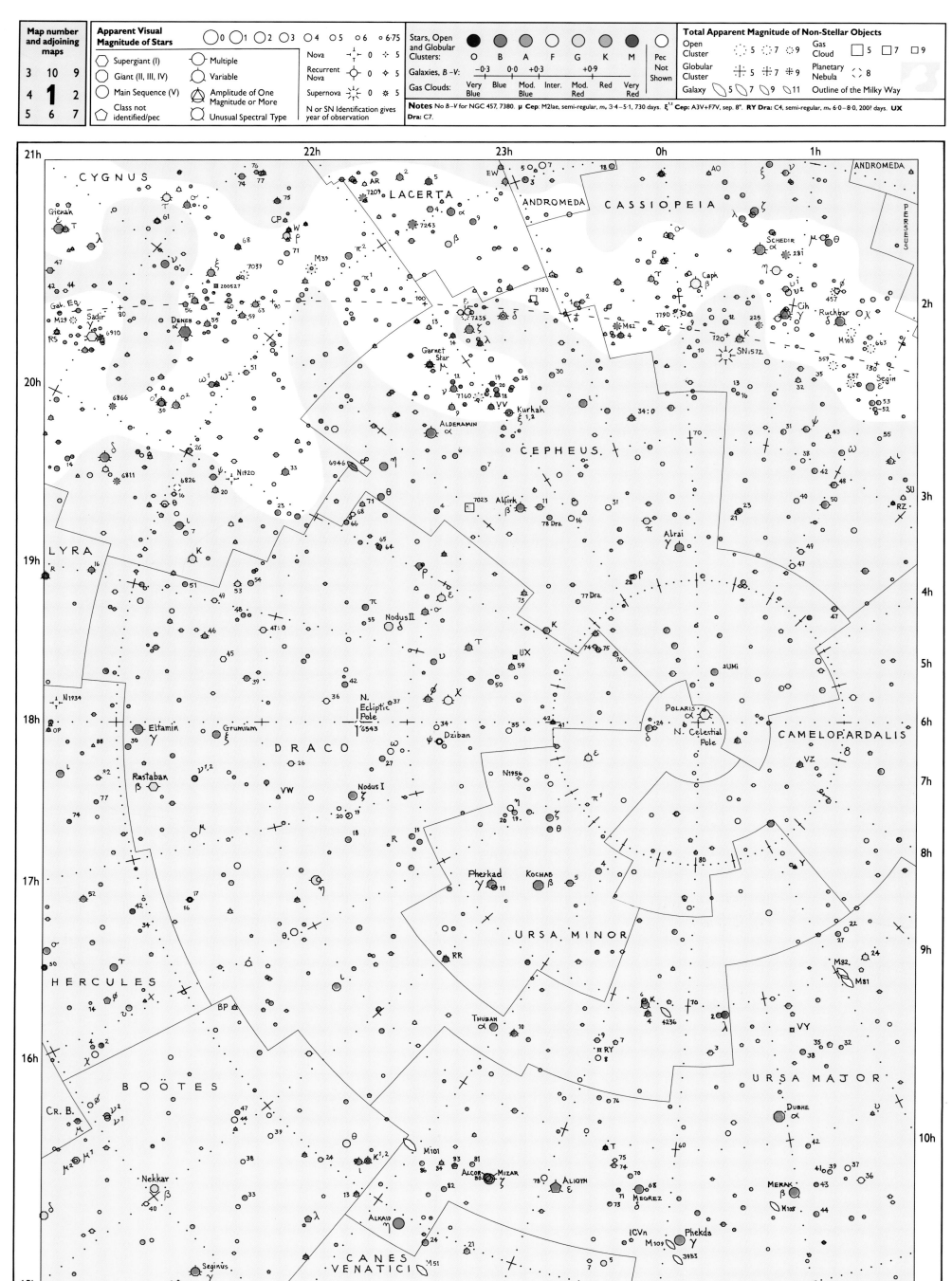

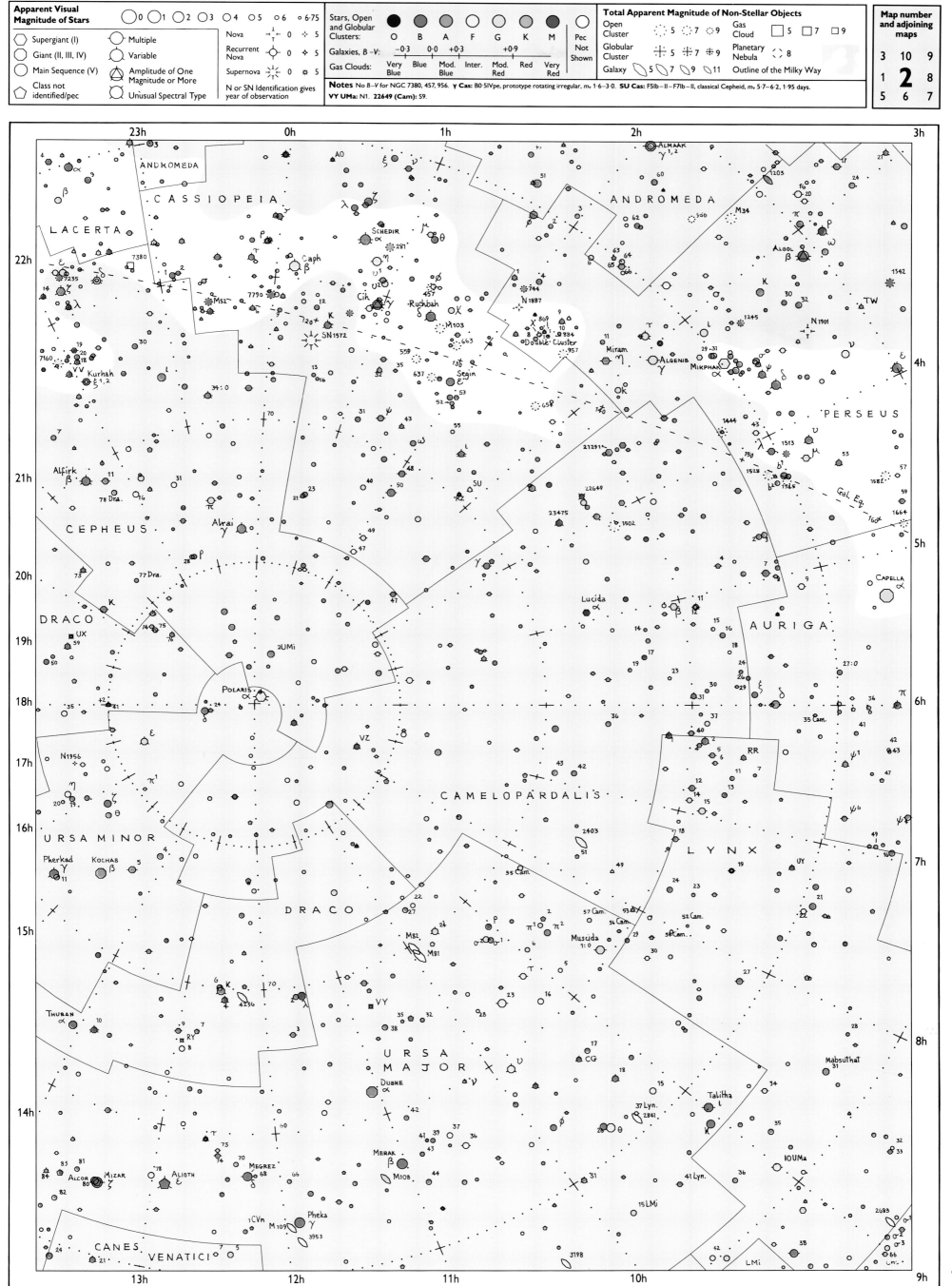

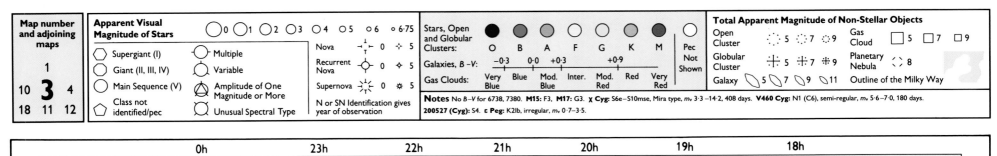

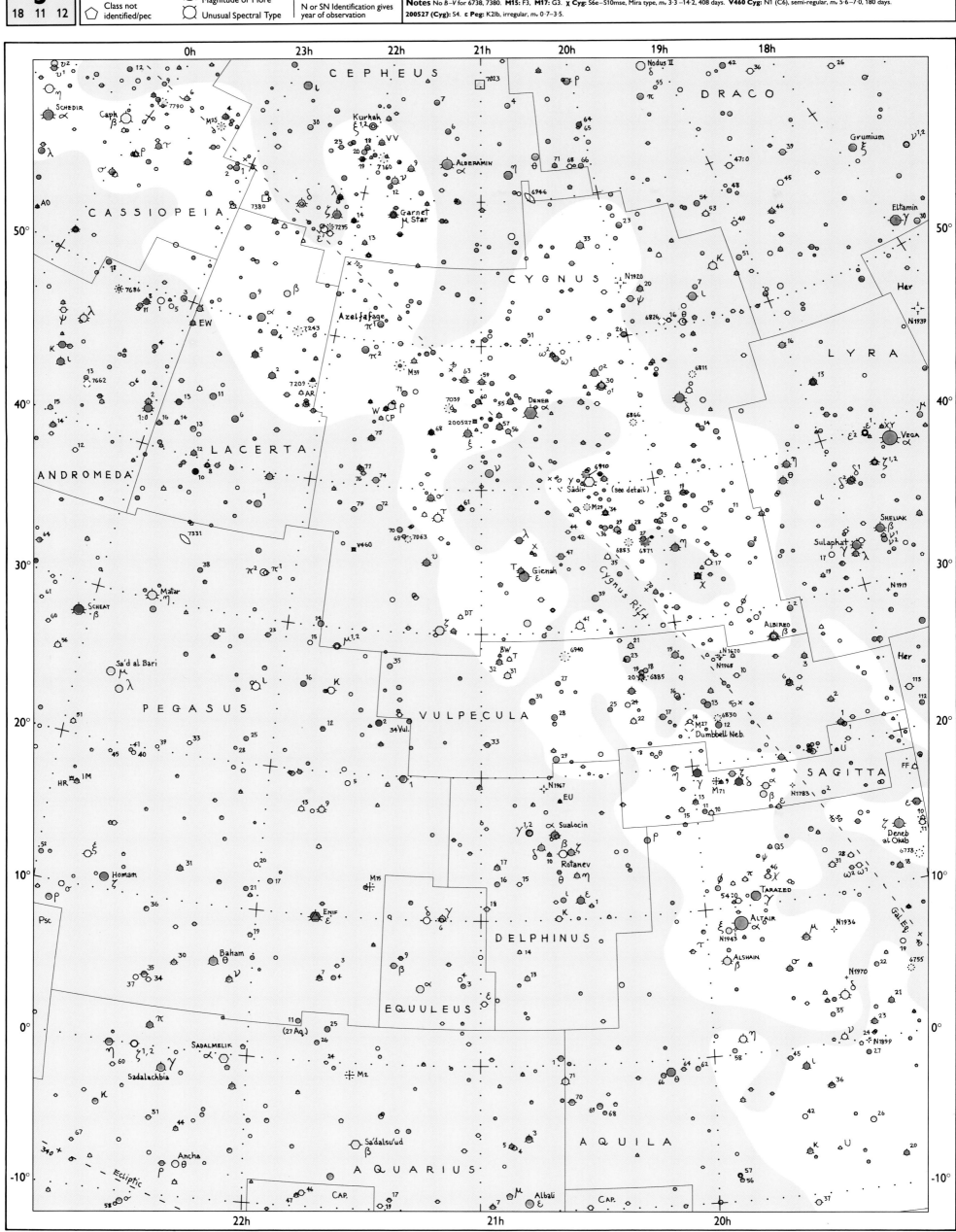

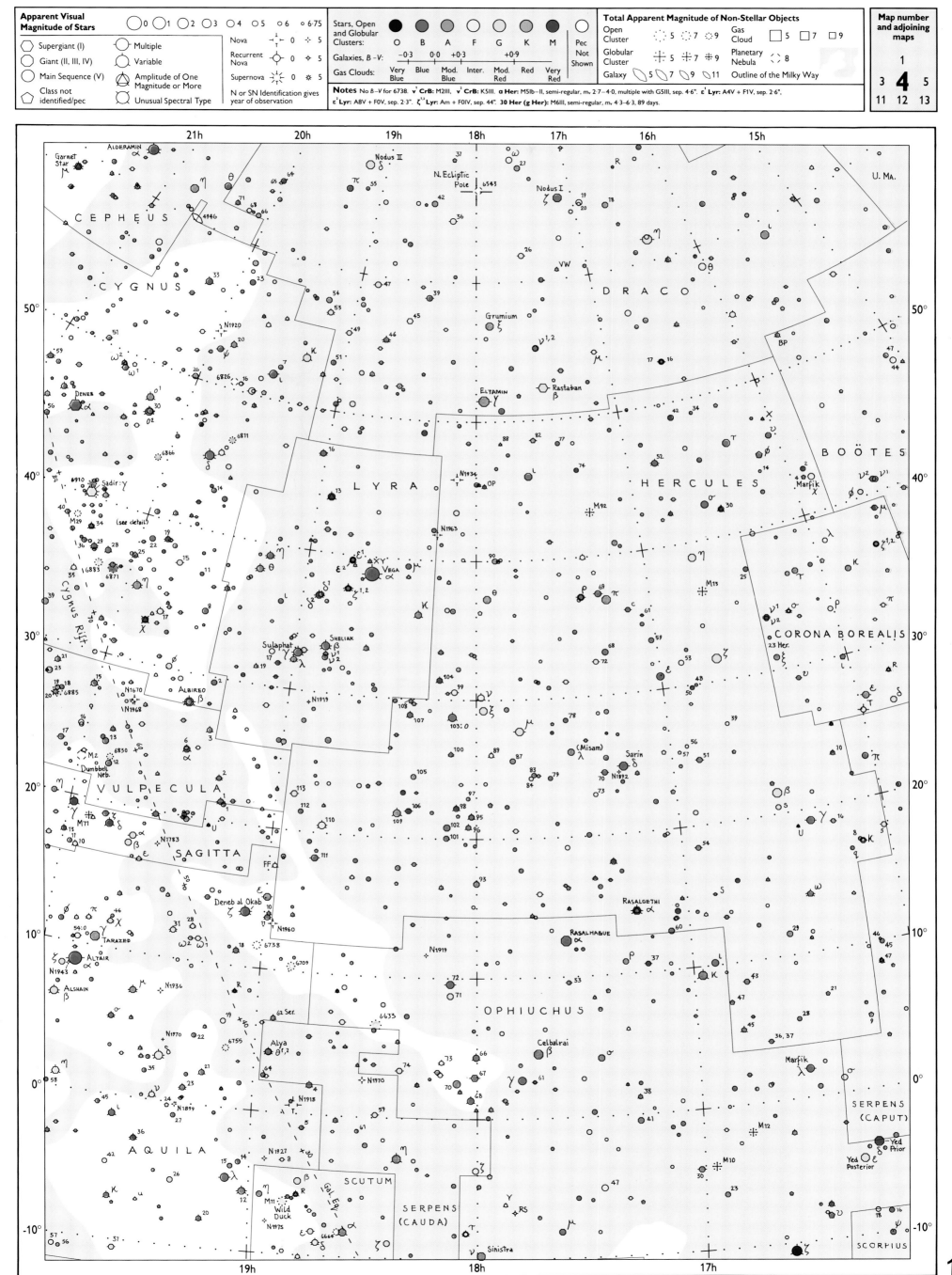

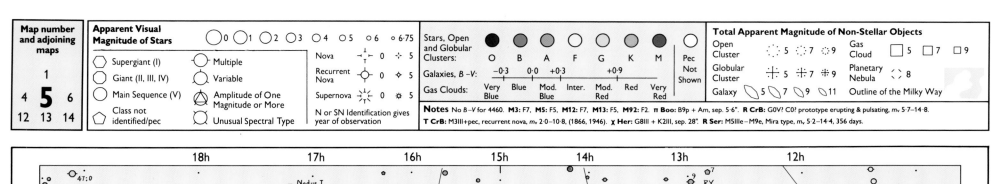

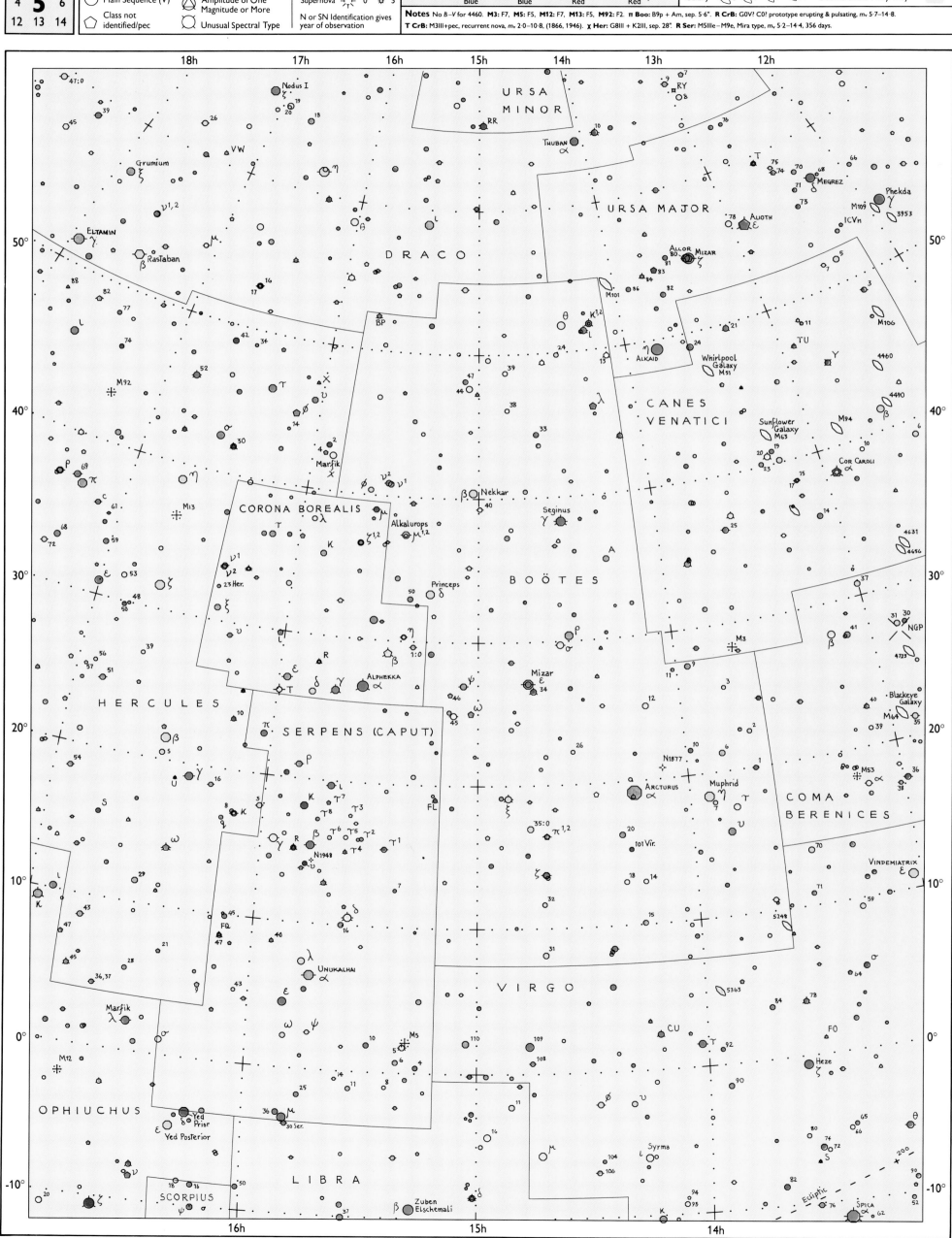

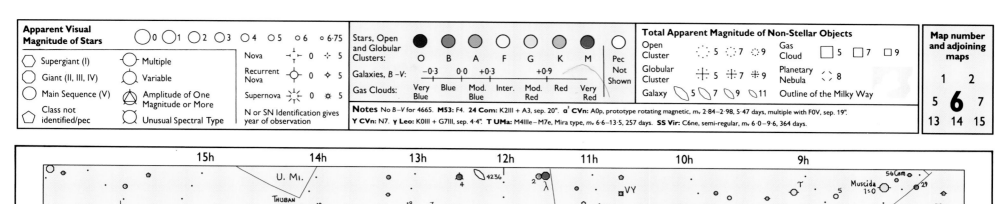

Apparent Visual Magnitude of Stars

○ 0 ○ 1 ○ 2 ○ 3 ○ 4 ○ 5 ○ 6 ○ 6·75

◇ Supergiant (I)   ◇ Multiple
◇ Giant (II, III, IV)   ◇ Variable
◇ Main Sequence (V)   △ Amplitude of One Magnitude or More
⬠ Class not identified/pec   ⬡ Unusual Spectral Type

Nova ⊥ 0 ÷ 5
Recurrent Nova ⊕ 0 ◇ 5
Supernova ✦ 0 ✧ 5

N or SN Identification gives year of observation

Stars, Open and Globular Clusters:
● ● ● ○ ○ ◐ ●   Pec Not Shown
O B A F G K M
Galaxies, B −V: −0·3 0·0 +0·3 +0·9
Gas Clouds: Very Blue | Blue | Mod. Blue | Inter. | Mod. Red | Red | Very Red

Total Apparent Magnitude of Non-Stellar Objects
Open Cluster ⠂⠂ 5 ⠂⠂ 7 ⠂⠂ 9
Globular Cluster ✦ 5 ✦ 7 ✦ 9
Galaxy ◯ 5 ◯ 7 ◯ 9 ◯ 11
Gas Cloud □ 5 □ 7 □ 9
Planetary Nebula ◇ 8
Outline of the Milky Way

Map number and adjoining maps
1	2
5	**6**	7
13	14	15

Notes No 8 −V for 4665. **M53:** F4. **24 Com:** K2III + A3, sep. 20". **α¹ CVn:** A0p, prototype rotating magnetic, m, 2·84−2·98, 5·47 days, multiple with F0V, sep. 19".
Y CVn: N7. **γ Leo:** K0III + G7III, sep. 4·4". **T UMa:** M4IIIe−M7e, Mira type, m, 6·6−13·5, 257 days. **SS Vir:** C6ne, semi-regular, m, 6·0−9·6, 364 days.

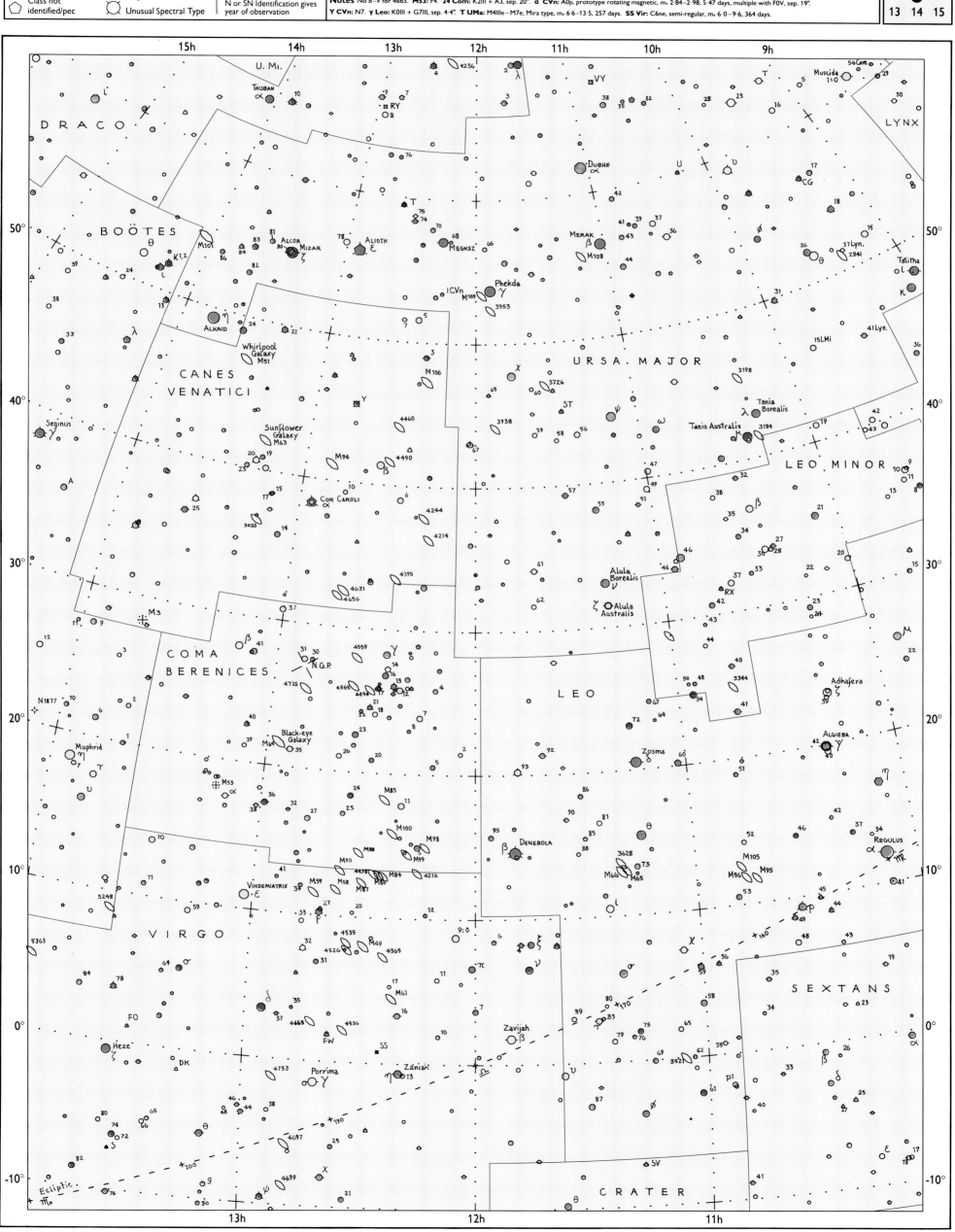

15

Apparent Visual Magnitude of Stars

○0 ○1 ○2 ○3 ○4 ∘5 ∘6 ∘6·75

Supergiant (I)
Giant (II, III, IV)
Main Sequence (V)
Class not identified/pec

Multiple
Variable
Amplitude of One Magnitude or More
Unusual Spectral Type

Nova · 0 ✢ 5
Recurrent Nova · 0 ✧ 5
Supernova ✳ 0 ✺ 5

N or SN Identification gives year of observation

Stars, Open and Globular Clusters:
O B A F G K M — Pec Not Shown

Galaxies, B −V: −0·3 (Very Blue) · 0·0 (Blue) · +0·3 (Mod. Blue) · (Inter.) · (Mod. Red) · +0·9 (Red) · (Very Red)

Gas Clouds:

Total Apparent Magnitude of Non-Stellar Objects

Open Cluster 5 7 9
Globular Cluster 5 7 9
Galaxy 5 7 9 11
Gas Cloud 5 7 9
Planetary Nebula 8
Outline of the Milky Way

Notes No B −V for 2231. **χ Cnc:** C5 (N3), semi-regular, m, 5·6–7·5, 195 days. **ζ¹·²Cnc:** F7 + G2 + 3 others. **α Gem:** A1V + AV + M1 + 2 others. **δ Gem:** K0III + 8' others.
γ¹ Leo: K0III, **γ² Leo:** G7III. **R Leo:** M6e-M9IIIe, Mira type, m, 4·4–11·3, 310 days.

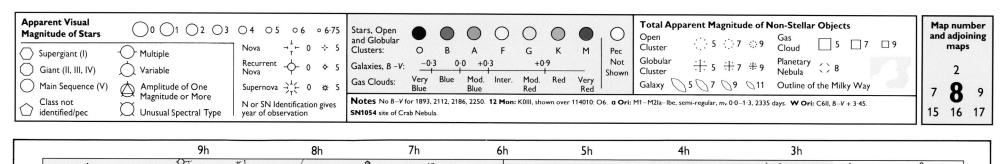

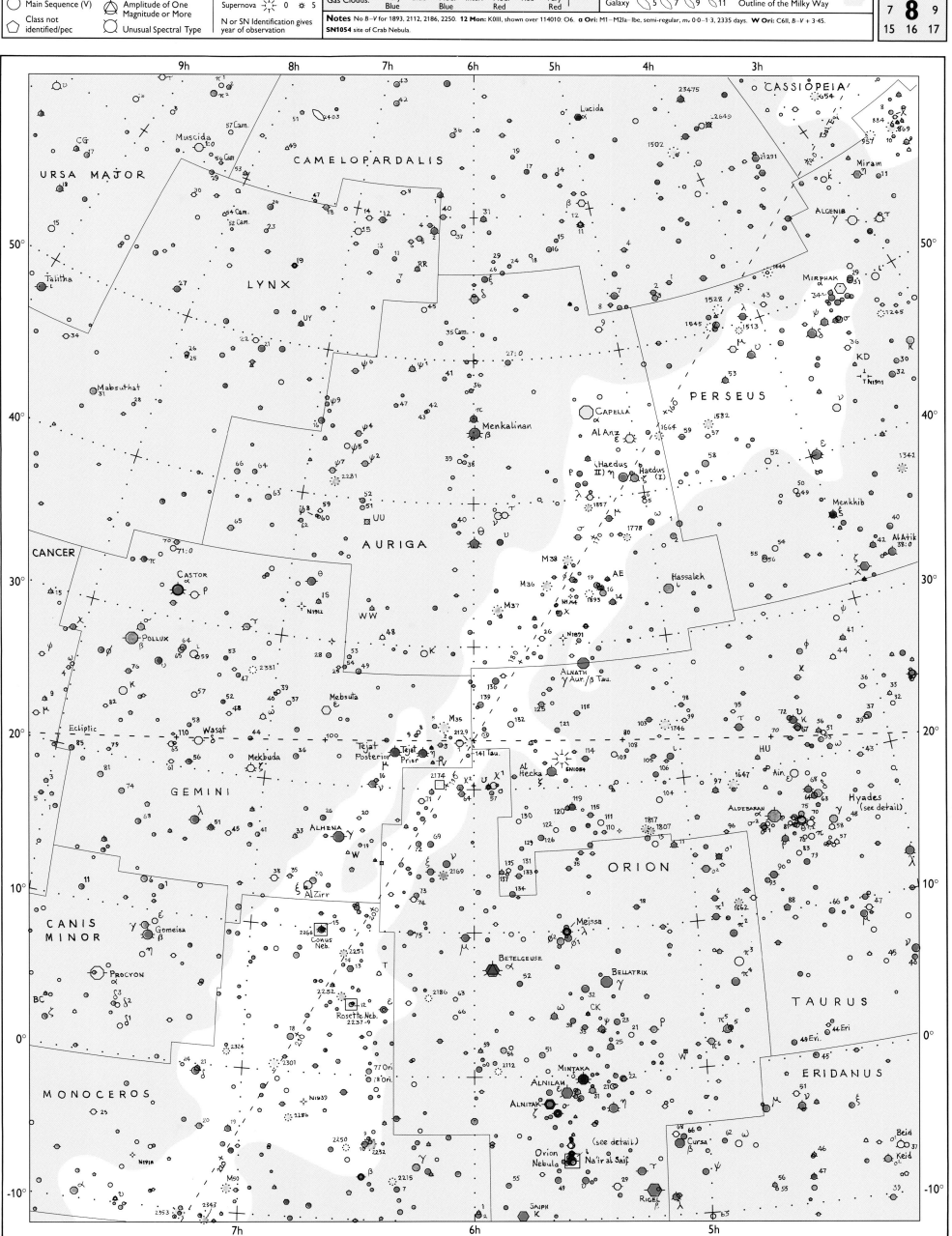

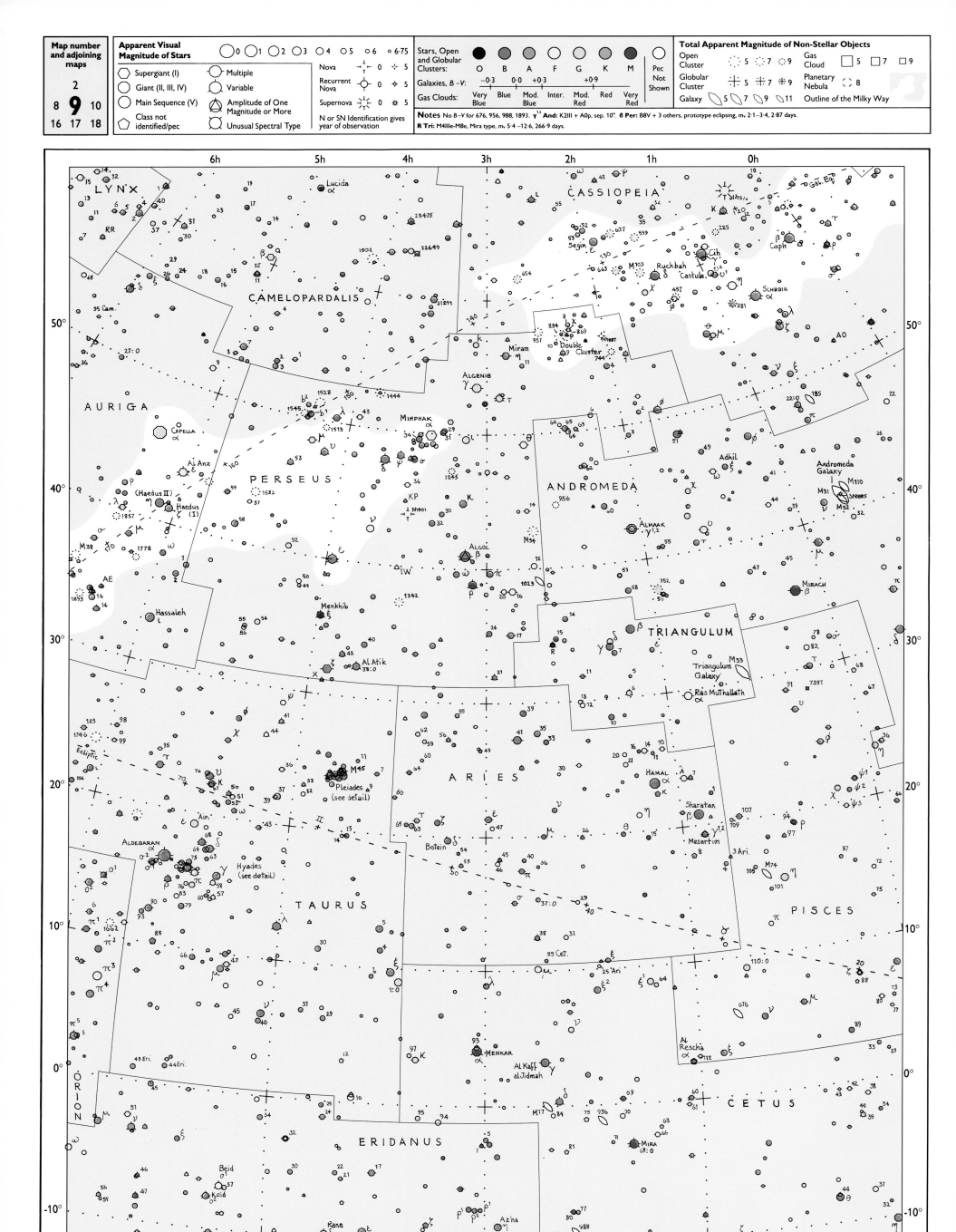

**Apparent Visual
Magnitude of Stars**

○ 0 ◯ 1 ◯ 2 ◯ 3 ○ 4 ○ 5 ○ 6 ○ 6·75

⬡ Supergiant (I)
⬡ Giant (II, III, IV)
◯ Main Sequence (V)
⬠ Class not
identified/pec

● Multiple
◉ Variable
◬ Amplitude of One
Magnitude or More
◯ Unusual Spectral Type

Nova ⊹ 0 ⋄ 5
Recurrent
Nova ⊕ 0 ✧ 5
Supernova ✳ 0 ✴ 5

N or SN Identification gives
year of observation

**Stars, Open
and Globular
Clusters:** ● ● ● ● ● ● ● ● ○ Pec
                O B A F G K M   Not
                                Shown

Galaxies, *B −V*:   −0·3 0·0 +0·3 +0·9
                        Very Blue Mod. Inter. Mod. Red Very
Gas Clouds: Blue   Blue   Red   Red

Total Apparent Magnitude of Non-Stellar Objects

Open
Cluster   ⬝5 ⬝7 ⬝9   Gas
                       Cloud   □5 □7 □9
Globular
Cluster   ⊕5 ⊕7 ⊕9   Planetary
                       Nebula ◇8
Galaxy   ⬠5 ⬠7 ⬠9 ⬠11 Outline of the Milky Way

Notes No *B −V* for 676, 956, 988, 1893. γ¹·² **And:** K2III + A0p, sep. 10″. **β Per:** B8V + 3 others, prototype eclipsing, *m*, 2·1–3·4, 2·87 days.
R Tri: M4IIIe-M8e, Mira type, *m*, 5·4 –12·6, 266·9 days.

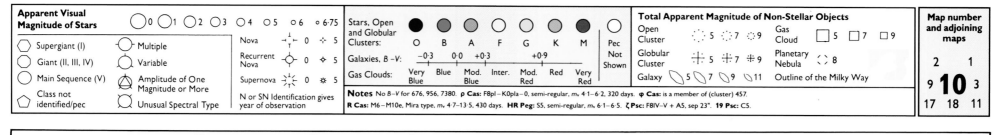

Apparent Visual Magnitude of Stars

○ 0 ○ 1 ○ 2 ○ 3 ○ 4 ○ 5 ○ 6 ∘ 6·75

◇ Supergiant (I)
◇ Giant (II, III, IV)
◇ Main Sequence (V)
⬠ Class not identified/pec

✛ Multiple
✱ Variable
△ Amplitude of One Magnitude or More
◯ Unusual Spectral Type

Nova   ⊹ 0 ⊹ 5
Recurrent Nova   ⊹ 0 ⊹ 5
Supernova   ✴ 0 ✴ 5

N or SN Identification gives year of observation

Stars, Open and Globular Clusters: ● O ● B ● A ○ F ○ G ○ K ● M   Pec Not Shown

Galaxies, B −V: −0·3 0·0 +0·3 +0·9

Gas Clouds: Very Blue Blue Mod. Blue Inter. Mod. Red Red Very Red

Total Apparent Magnitude of Non-Stellar Objects

Open Cluster   ⁙ 5 ⁙ 7 ⁙ 9
Globular Cluster   ✦ 5 ✦ 7 ✦ 9
Galaxy   ◯ 5 ◯ 7 ◯ 9 ◯ 11

Gas Cloud   □ 5 □ 7 □ 9
Planetary Nebula   ◇ 8
Outline of the Milky Way

Map number and adjoining maps

2	1	
9	**10**	3
17	18	11

Notes No B−V for 676, 956, 7380. ρ Cas: F8pl−K0pla−0, semi-regular, m, 4·1−6·2, 320 days. φ Cas: is a member of (cluster) 457.
R Cas: M6−M10e, Mira type, m, 4·7−13·5, 430 days. HR Peg: S5, semi-regular, m, 6·1−6·5. ζ Psc: F8IV−V + A5, sep 23″. 19 Psc: C5.

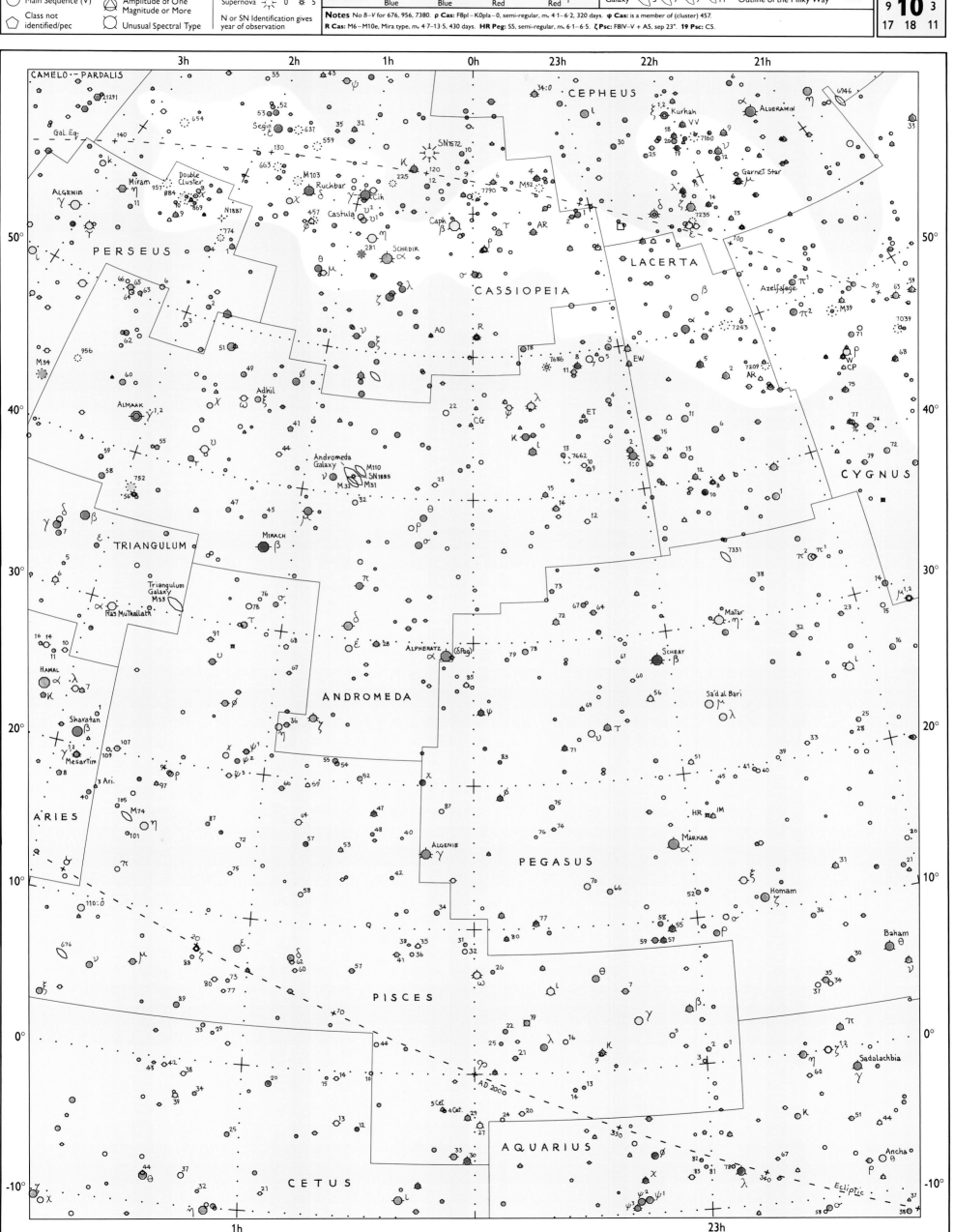

Celestial Equator (top) and Galactic Equator (bottom)

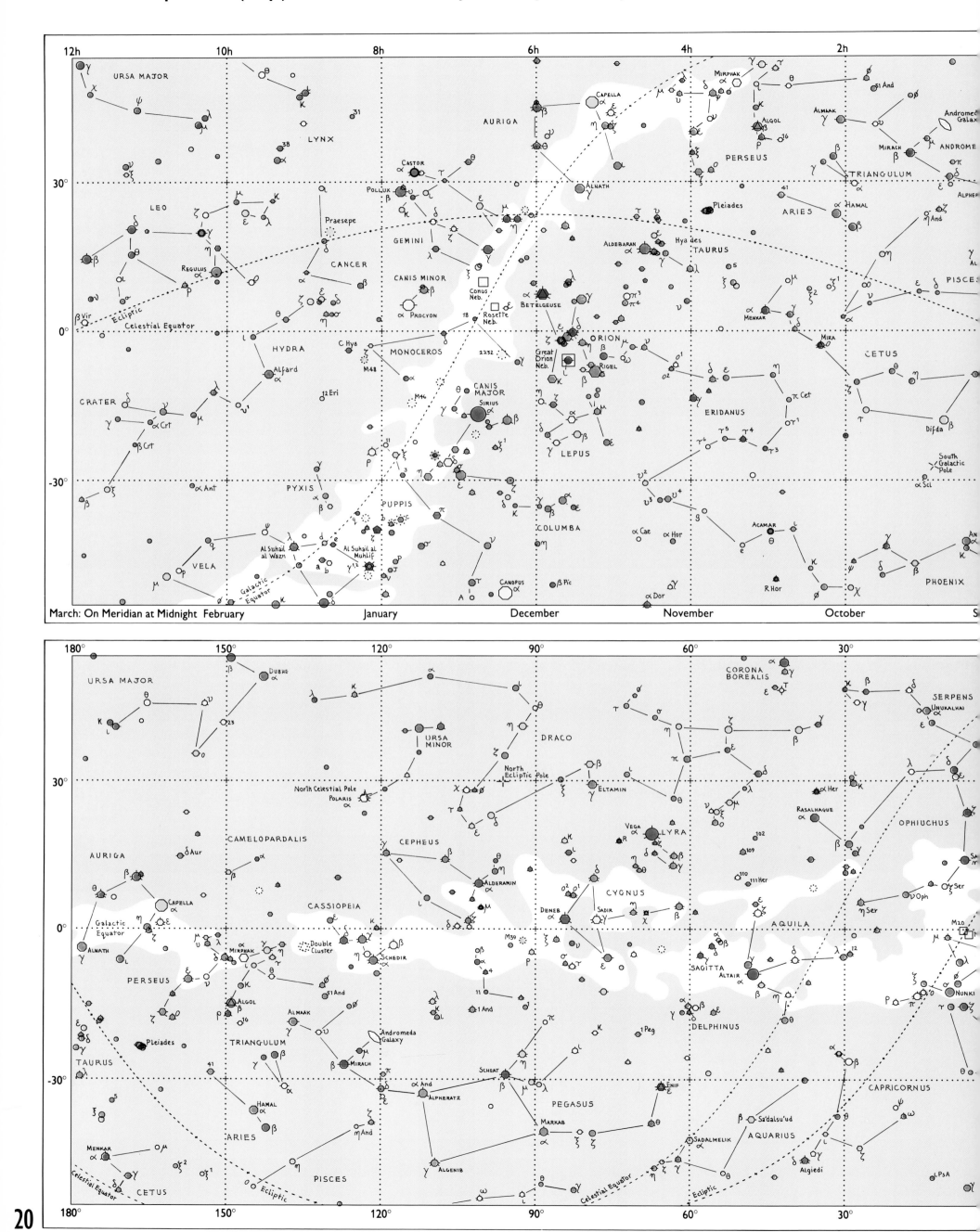

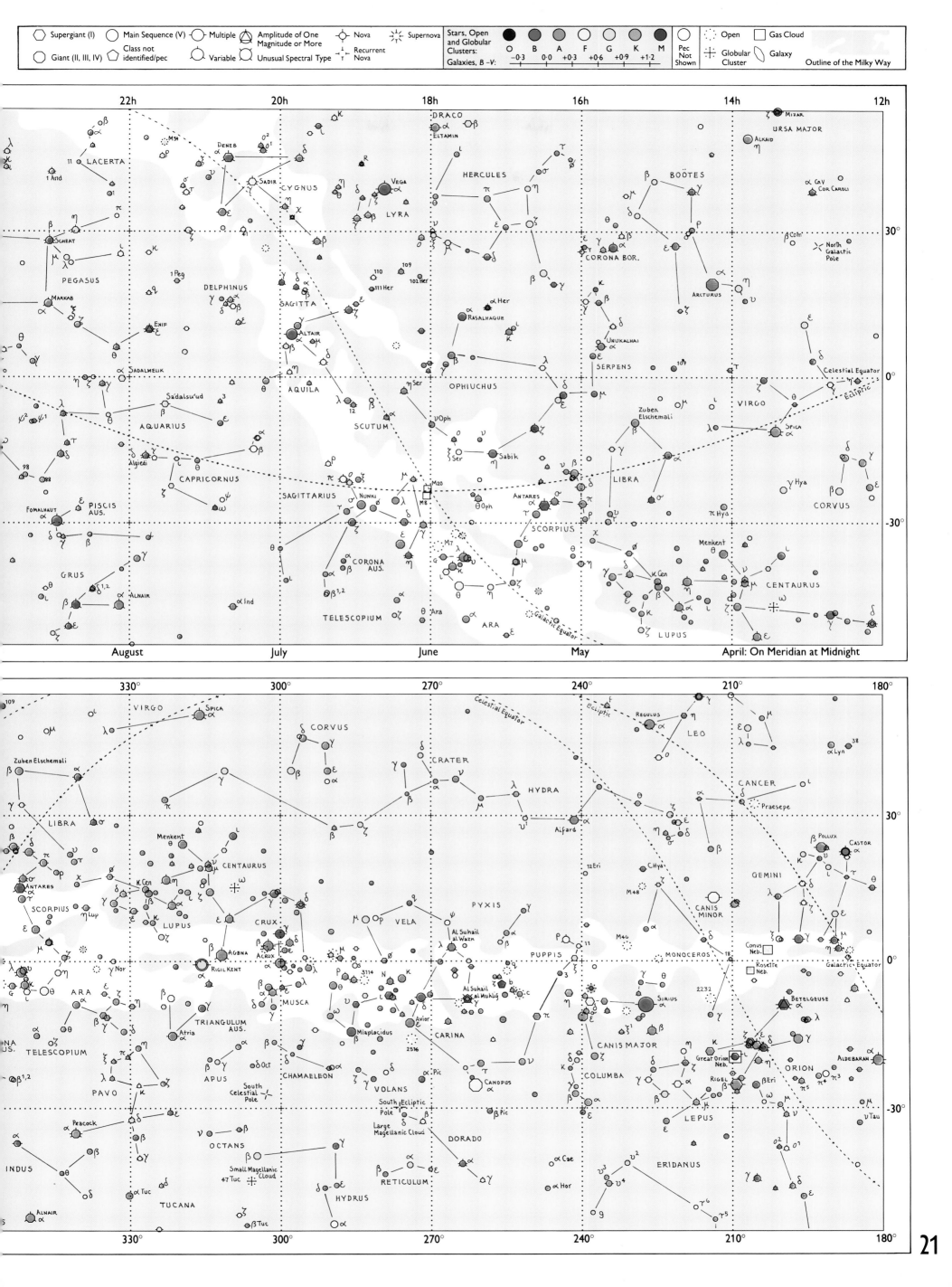

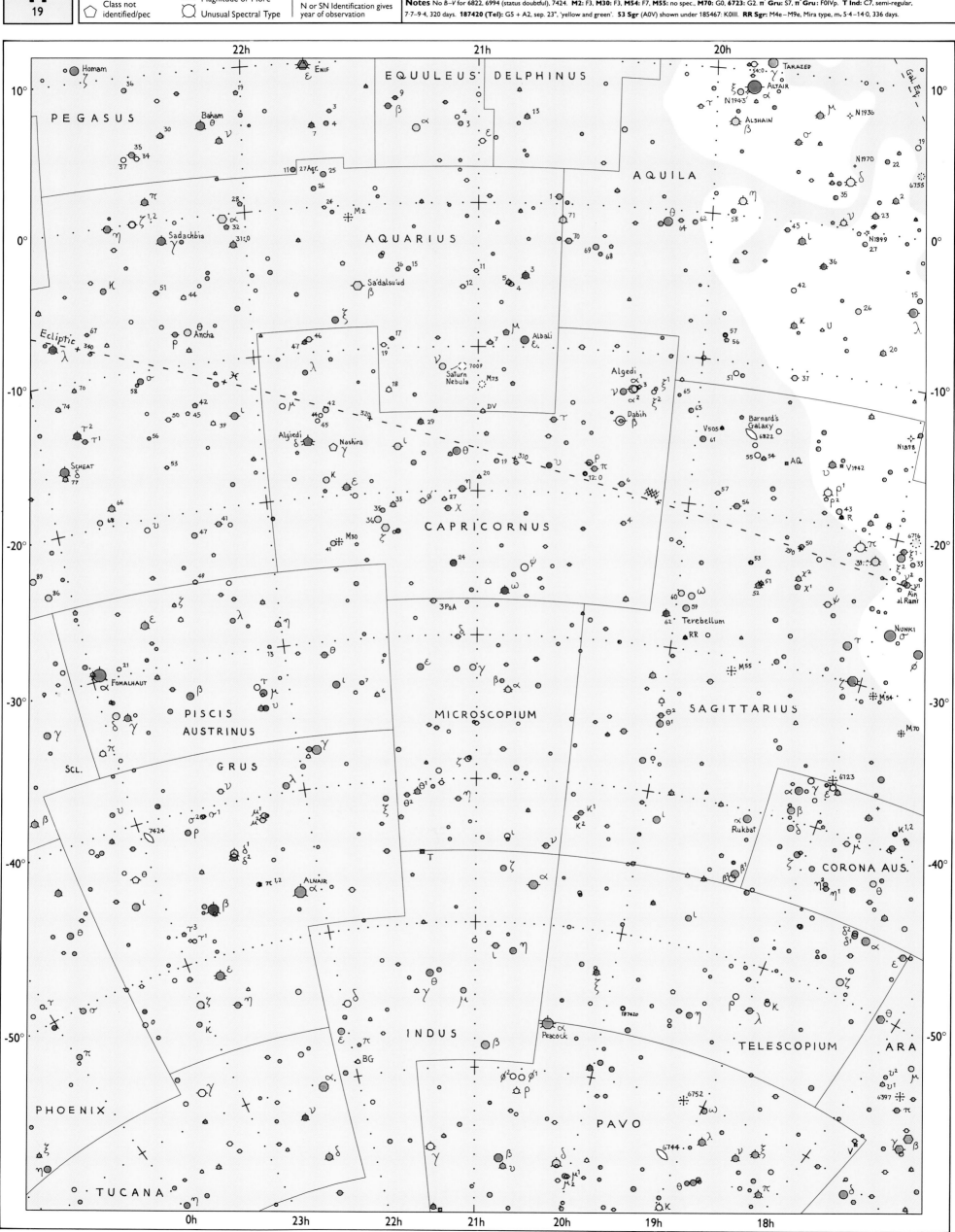

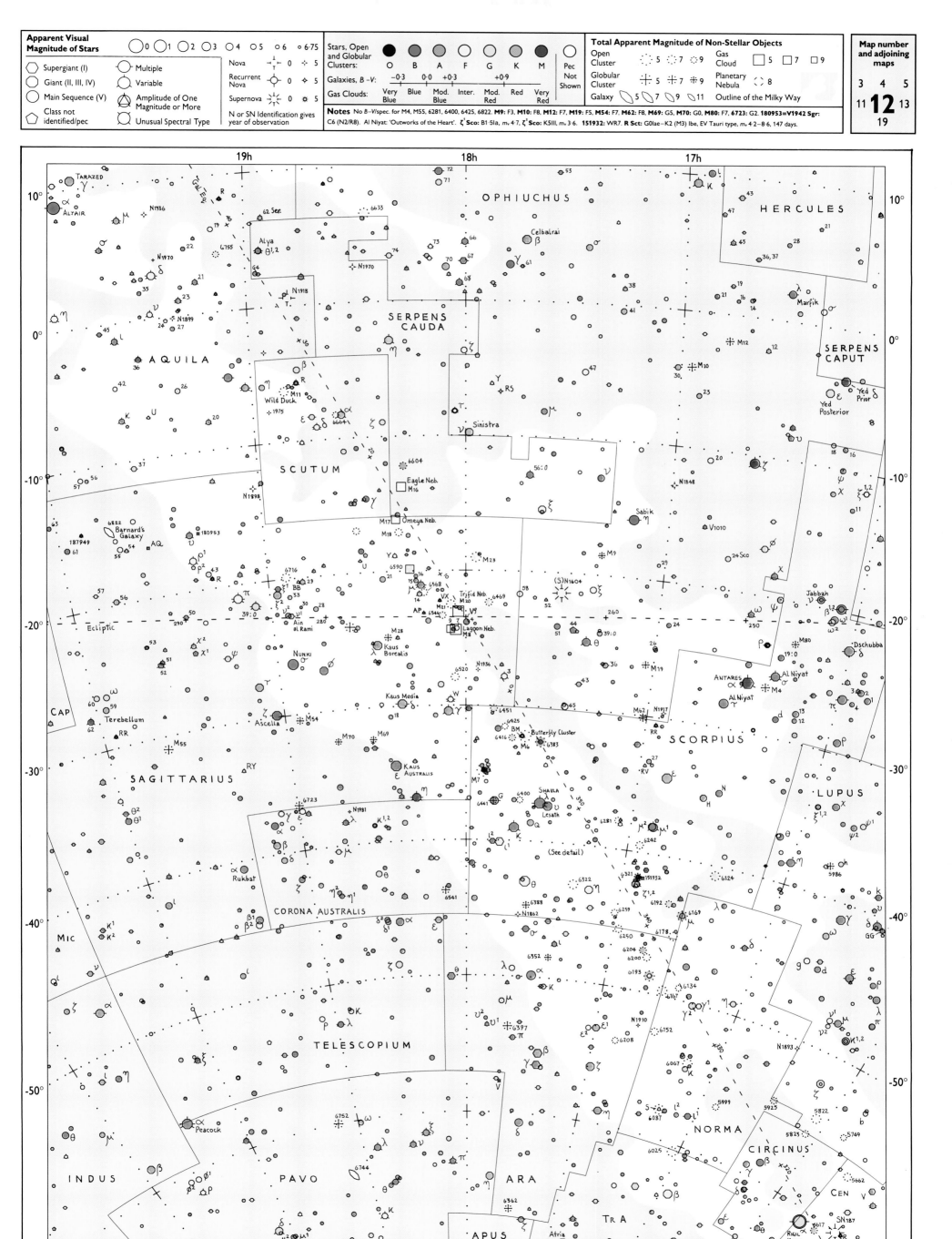

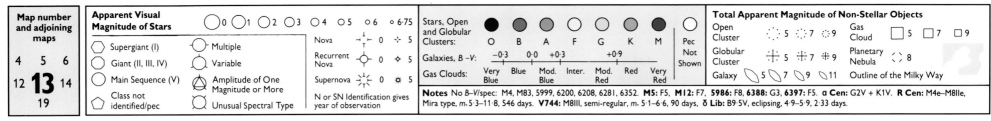

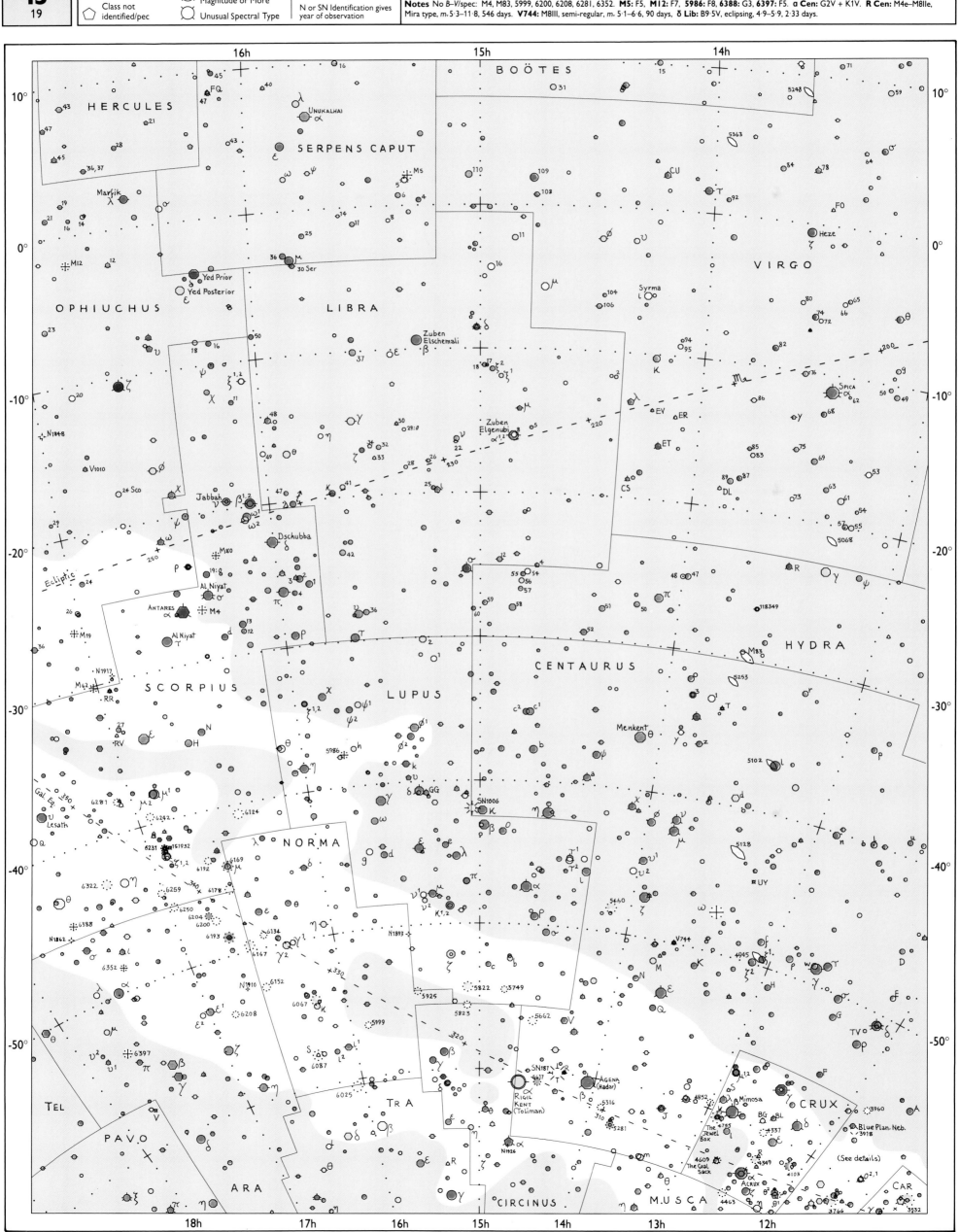

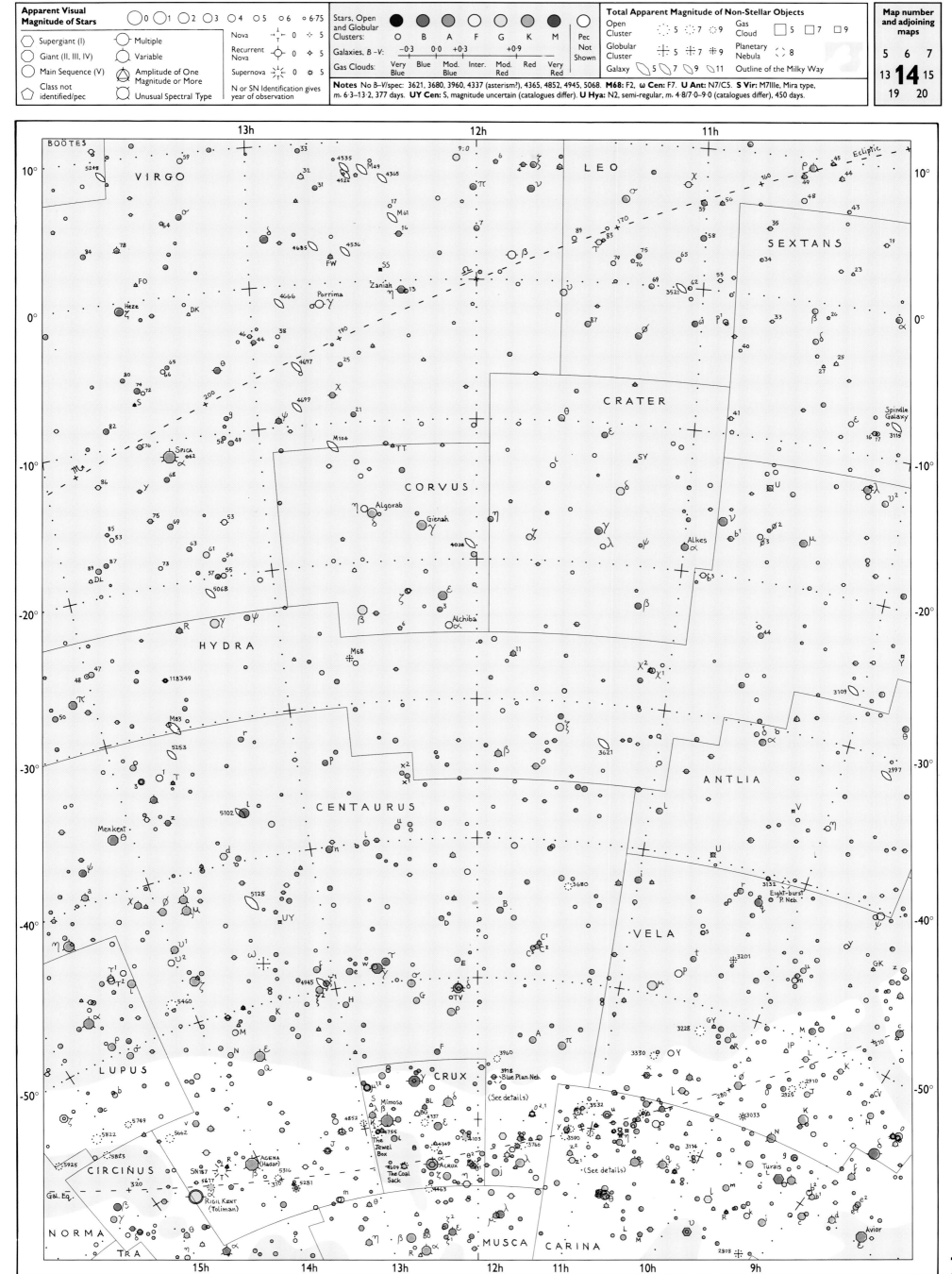

Map number and adjoining maps

6	7	8
14	**15**	16
	20	

Apparent Visual Magnitude of Stars

○ 0 ○ 1 ○ 2 ○ 3 ○ 4 ○ 5 ○ 6 · 6·75

⬡ Supergiant (I)   ◇ Multiple
◯ Giant (II, III, IV)   ◯ Variable
◯ Main Sequence (V)   △ Amplitude of One Magnitude or More
⬠ Class not identified/pec   ◯ Unusual Spectral Type

Nova   –1 ○ 0 ◇
Recurrent Nova   –1 ○ 0 ◇
Supernova   –1 ☆ 0 ☆

N or SN Identification gives year of observation

Stars, Open and Globular Clusters:
● O   ● B   ○ A   ○ F   ○ G   ● K   ● M   ○ Pec Not Shown

Galaxies, B –V: –0·3   0·0   +0·3   +0·9

Gas Clouds: Very Blue   Blue   Mod. Blue   Inter.   Mod. Red   Red   Very Red

Total Apparent Magnitude of Non-Stellar Objects

Open Cluster   ⊙ 5   ⊙ 7   ⊙ 9
Globular Cluster   ✛ 5   ✛ 7   ✛ 9
Galaxy   ◯ 5   ◯ 7   ◯ 9   ◯ 11

Gas Cloud   ▢ 5   ▢ 7   ▢ 9
Planetary Nebula   ◇ 8
Outline of the Milky Way

Notes No B–V/spec: 2414, 2421, 2482, 2527, 2579, 2587, 2627, 2997, 3033, 3109, 3114, 3201. **2808:** F8. **U Mon:** F8e–K0Ibp, RV Tauri type, m. 6·1–8·1, 92 days. **88539:** N7. **v⁴ Pup:** B3 + B3 + A0. **51208:** N7. **RS Pup:** F9–G7, classical Cepheid, 6·5–7·7, 41·4 days. **T Pyx:** Pec, 6·3–14·0, 1890, 1902, 1920, 1944, 1966.

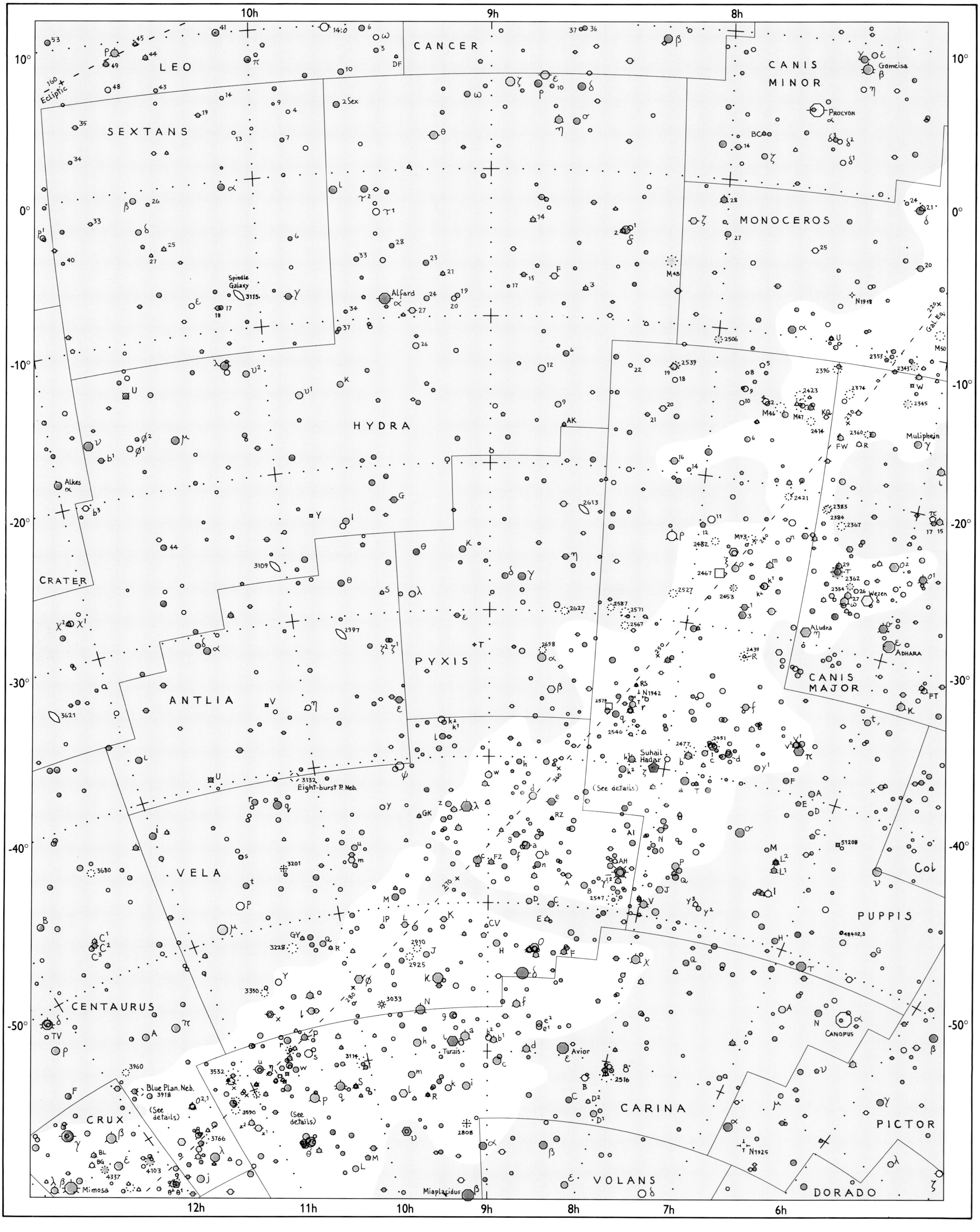

LEO
SEXTANS
CANCER
CANIS MINOR
MONOCEROS
HYDRA
CRATER
PYXIS
ANTLIA
CANIS MAJOR
VELA
PUPPIS
CENTAURUS
CARINA
CRUX
PICTOR
VOLANS
DORADO

Spindle Galaxy 3115
Alfard
Alkes
Eight-burst P. Neb. 3132
Blue Plan. Neb. 3918
Procyon
Gomeisa
M48
N 1918
M50
Muliphein
Wezen
Aludra
Adhara
Suhail Hadar
Turais
Avior
Canopus
Mimosa
Miaplacidus

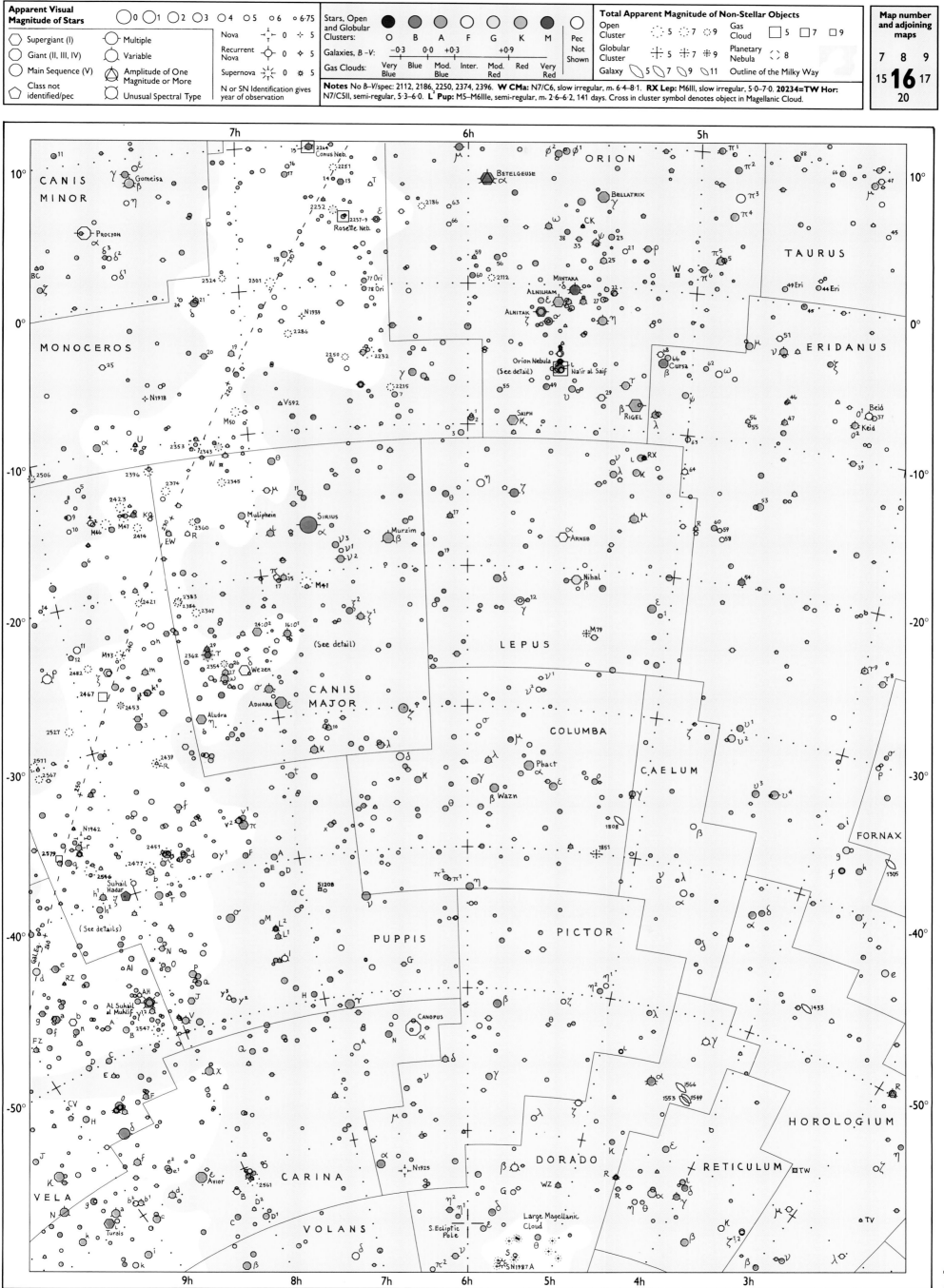

Apparent Visual Magnitude of Stars

0 1 2 3 4 5 6 6·75

Supergiant (I)   Multiple
Giant (II, III, IV)   Variable
Main Sequence (V)   Amplitude of One Magnitude or More
Class not identified/pec   Unusual Spectral Type

Nova   0
Recurrent Nova 0 5
Supernova   0 5

N or SN Identification gives year of observation

Stars, Open and Globular Clusters: O B A F G K M Pec Not Shown

Galaxies, B–V: −0·3 0·0 +0·3 +0·9

Gas Clouds: Very Blue / Blue / Mod. Blue / Inter. / Mod. Red / Red / Very Red

Total Apparent Magnitude of Non-Stellar Objects

Open Cluster 5 7 9	Gas Cloud 5 7 9	
Globular Cluster 5 7 9	Planetary Nebula 8	
Galaxy 5 7 9 11	Outline of the Milky Way	

Notes No B–V/spec: 2112, 2186, 2250, 2374, 2396. **W CMa:** N7/C6, slow irregular, m. 6·4–8·1. **RX Lep:** M6III, slow irregular, 5·0–7·0. **20234=TW Hor:** N7/C5II, semi-regular, 5·3–6·0. **L² Pup:** M5–M6IIIe, semi-regular, m. 2·6–6·2, 141 days. Cross in cluster symbol denotes object in Magellanic Cloud.

CANIS MINOR
MONOCEROS
ORION
TAURUS
ERIDANUS
CANIS MAJOR
LEPUS
COLUMBA
CAELUM
FORNAX
PUPPIS
PICTOR
CARINA
VELA
VOLANS
DORADO
HOROLOGIUM
RETICULUM

Procyon
Gomeisa
Betelgeuse
Bellatrix
Mintaka
Alnilham
Alnitak
Orion Nebula (See detail)
Na'ir al Saif
Saiph
Rigel
Cursa
Beid
Keid
Sirius
Muliphein
Murzim
Arneb
Nihal
M79
Adhara
Wezen
Aludra
Phact
Wazn
Canopus
Avior
Turais
Suhail Hadar
Al Suhail al Muhlif
Large Magellanic Cloud
S. Ecliptic Pole
SN1987A

27

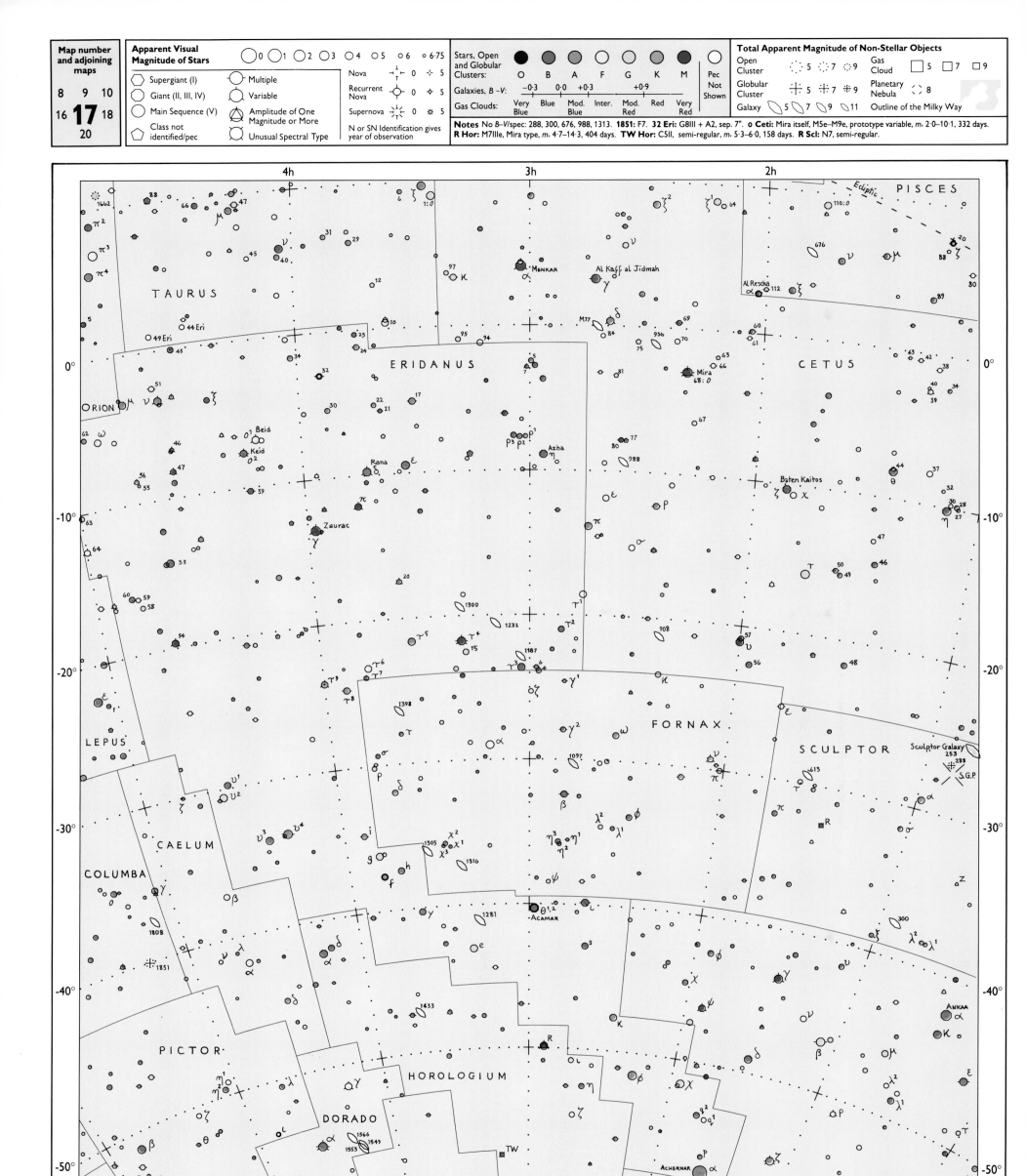

Apparent Visual Magnitude of Stars

0 1 2 3 4 5 6 6·75

- ⬡ Supergiant (I)
- ⬡ Giant (II, III, IV)
- ◯ Main Sequence (V)
- ⬠ Class not identified/pec
- ◯ Multiple
- ◯ Variable
- △ Amplitude of One Magnitude or More
- ◯ Unusual Spectral Type

Nova   0   5
Recurrent Nova   0   5
Supernova   0   5

N or SN Identification gives year of observation

Stars, Open and Globular Clusters: O B A F G K M   Pec Not Shown

Galaxies, B −V: −0·3   0·0   +0·3   +0·9

Gas Clouds: Very Blue   Blue   Mod. Blue   Inter.   Mod. Red   Red   Very Red

Total Apparent Magnitude of Non-Stellar Objects

Open Cluster 5 7 9	Gas Cloud 5 7 9
Globular Cluster 5 7 9	Planetary Nebula 8
Galaxy 5 7 9 11	Outline of the Milky Way

Notes No *B−V*/spec: 288, 300, 676, 988, 1313. **1851**: F7. **32 Eri**: G8III + A2, sep. 7". **o Ceti**: Mira itself, M5e–M9e, prototype variable, *m.* 2·0–10·1, 332 days. **R Hor**: M7IIIe, Mira type, *m.* 4·7–14·3, 404 days. **TW Hor**: C5II, semi-regular, *m.* 5·3–6·0, 158 days. **R Scl**: N7, semi-regular.

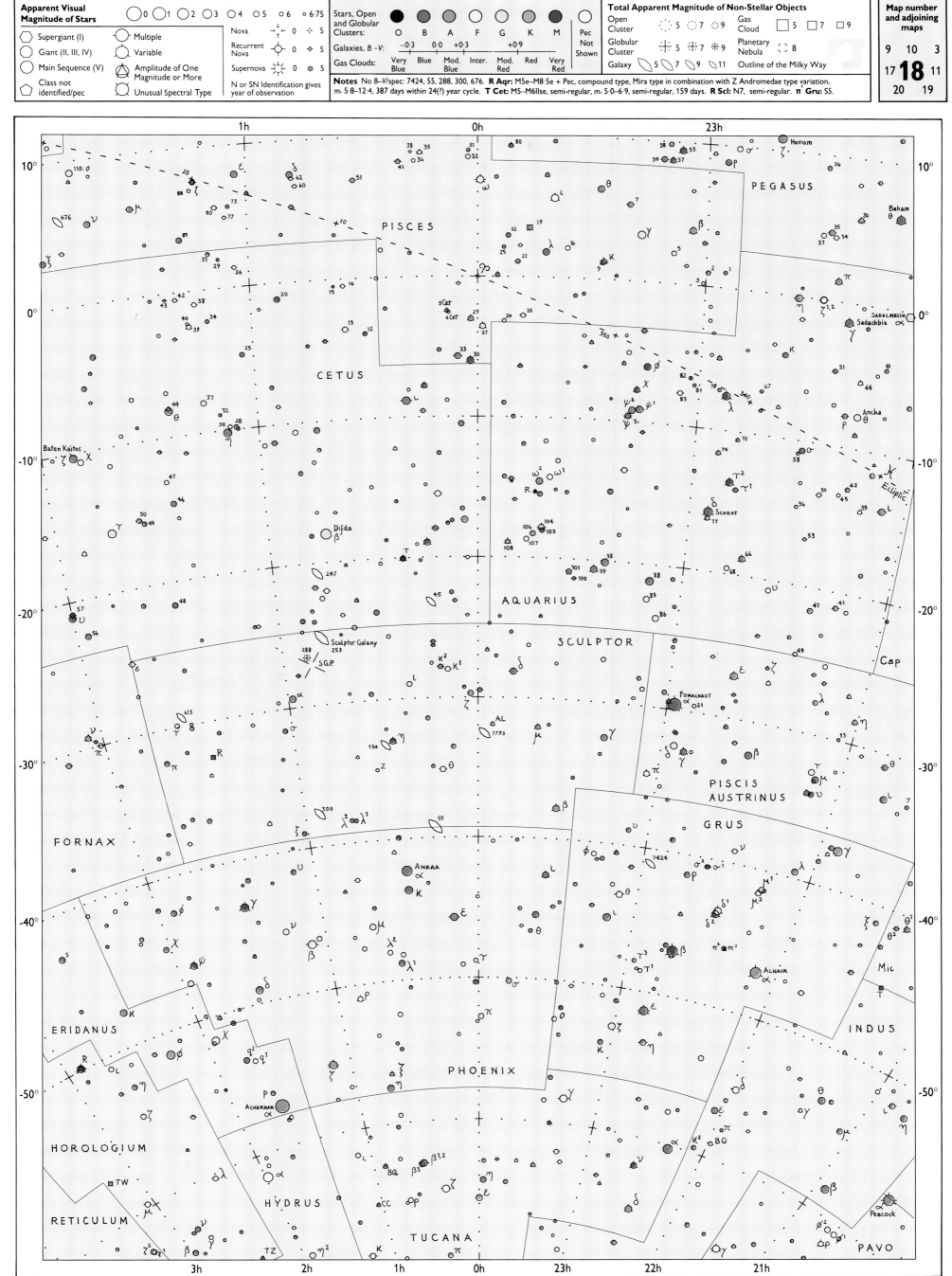

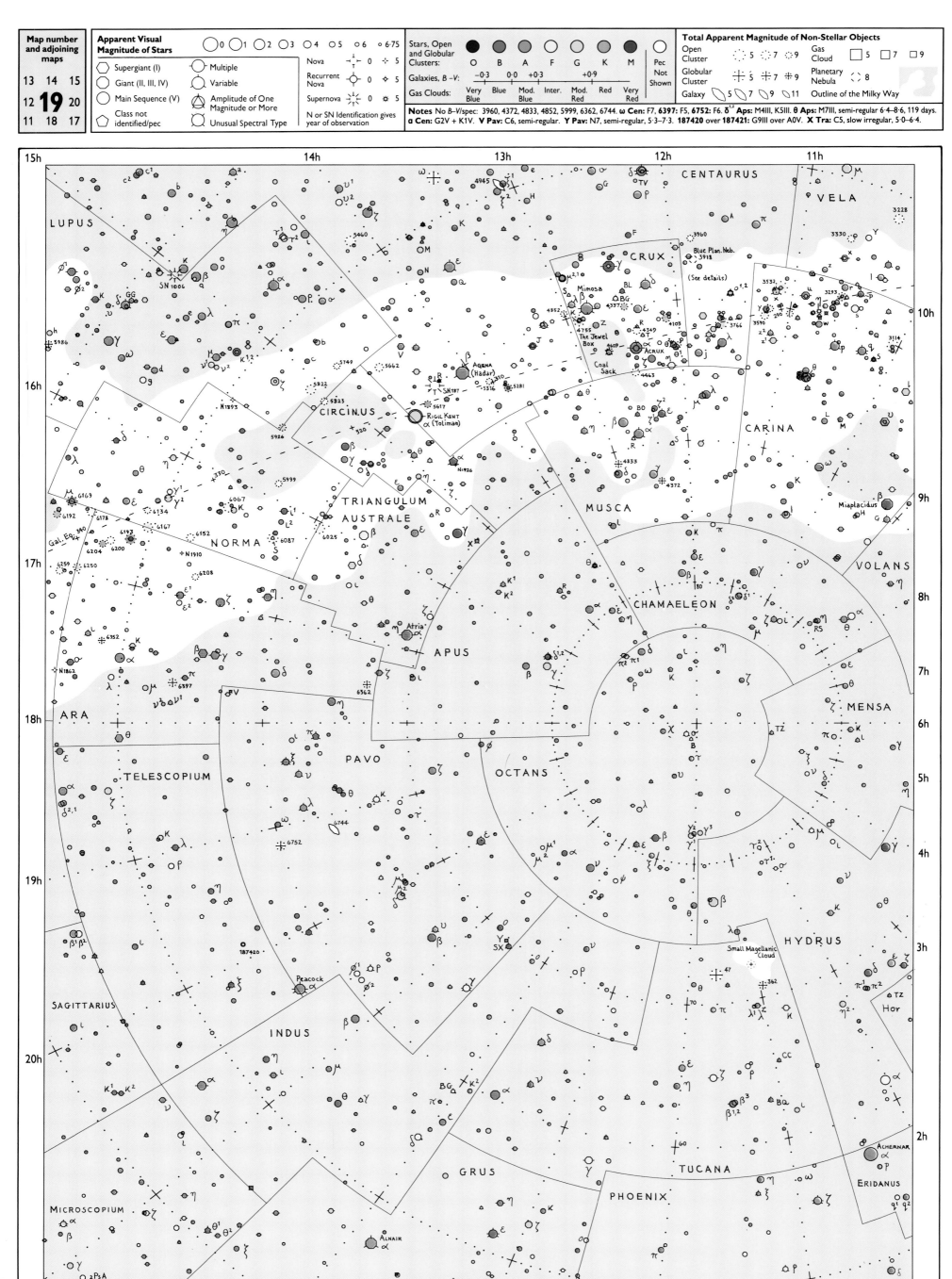

Apparent Visual Magnitude of Stars 0 1 2 3 4 5 6 6·75

Supergiant (I) · Giant (II, III, IV) · Main Sequence (V) · Class not identified/pec

Multiple · Variable · Amplitude of One Magnitude or More · Unusual Spectral Type

Nova 0 5 · Recurrent Nova 0 5 · Supernova 0 5

N or SN Identification gives year of observation

Stars, Open and Globular Clusters:	O	B	A	F	G	K	M	Pec Not Shown
Galaxies, B −V:	−0·3	0·0	+0·3		+0·9			
Gas Clouds:	Very Blue	Blue	Mod. Blue	Inter.	Mod. Red	Red	Very Red	

Total Apparent Magnitude of Non-Stellar Objects

Open Cluster 5 7 9 · Gas Cloud 5 7 9

Globular Cluster 5 7 9 · Planetary Nebula 8

Galaxy 5 7 9 11 · Outline of the Milky Way

Notes No *B–V*/spec: 1313, 2442, 3033, 3960, 4372, 4833, 4852. **47 Tuc:** G3, **362:** F8. **R Dor:** M8IIIqe, semi-regular, *m.* 4·8–6·6, 338 days. **θ^1 Tuc:** B8V, **θ^2 Tuc:** A2V, **θ^3 Tuc:** A2V. Cross in cluster symbol denotes object in Magellanic Cloud.

Map number and adjoining maps

13 14 15
19 **20** 16
11 18 17

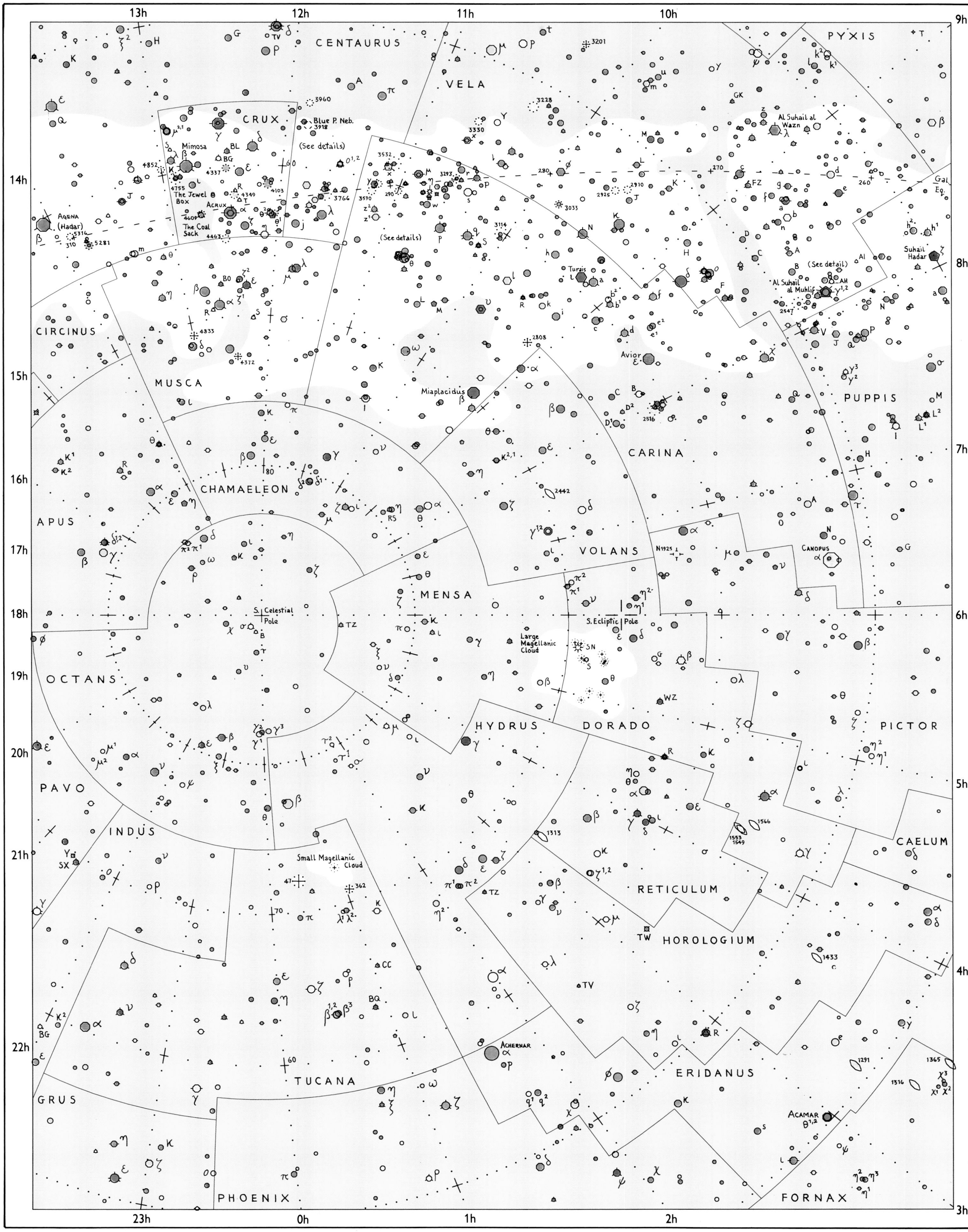

CENTAURUS
VELA
PYXIS
CRUX
Mimosa
The Jewel Box
Acrux
The Coal Sack
Blue P. Neb.
Agena (Hadar)
CIRCINUS
MUSCA
CARINA
PUPPIS
Al Suhail al Wazn
Suhail Hadar
Al Suhail al Muhlif
Turais
Avior
Miaplacidus
Canopus
APUS
CHAMAELEON
VOLANS
S. Celestial Pole
MENSA
S. Ecliptic Pole
Large Magellanic Cloud
OCTANS
HYDRUS
DORADO
PICTOR
PAVO
INDUS
CAELUM
Small Magellanic Cloud
RETICULUM
HOROLOGIUM
Achernar
GRUS
TUCANA
ERIDANUS
Acamar
PHOENIX
FORNAX
(See details)
13h
12h
11h
10h
9h
8h
7h
6h
5h
4h
3h
14h
15h
16h
17h
18h
19h
20h
21h
22h
23h
0h
1h
2h

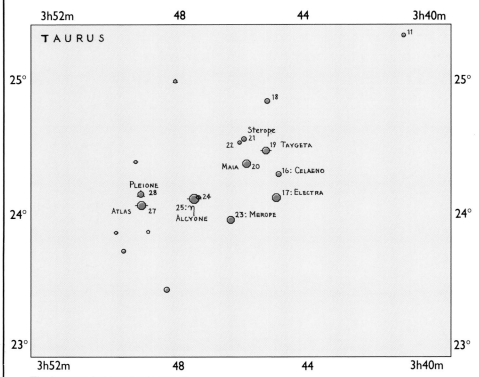

The Pleiades: 2½° field (main map 9)
'The Seven Sisters', M45, an open cluster of earliest spectral type B about 400 light years away, and a famous test of eyesight since classical times. The Pleiades were the daughters of Atlas and Pleione. Their name translates as the 'sailing ones' – during the sailing season in around 1000 BC, which lasted from May to October, the Pleiades would be seen to rise, but not to set.

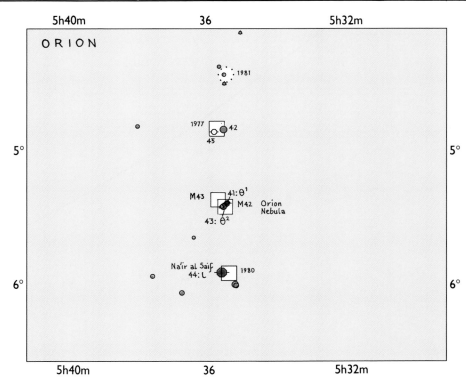

Orion's Sword: 2½° field (main maps 8, 16)
The 'Great Nebula' in Orion, extending from M42 to NGC 1980, is centred on the Trapezium cluster of four stars (θ¹A, pec; θ¹B, O; θ¹C, O6p; θ¹D, B0·5p) which can be separated with a small telescope. Because of the convention whereby gas clouds are listed according to the magnitude of the associated star, NGC 1980, associated with ι Ori (O9III, m. 2·76), stands in for the Orion Nebula in the main series of maps.

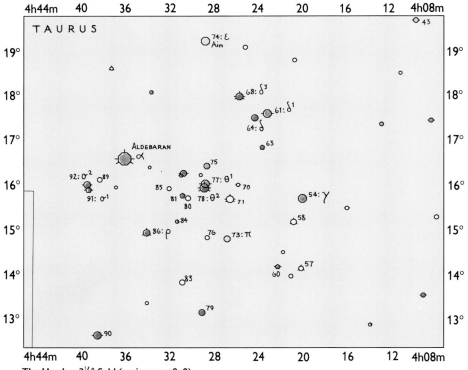

The Hyades: 2½° field (main maps 8, 9)
At 150 light years away, the Hyades ('rainmakers') are the nearest open cluster to the Sun. By measuring their motions, it can be shown that Aldebaran, α Tauri, is not a true member of the cluster, and lies at only half the distance. The earliest members of the cluster are of spectral type A; ε Tauri (G9III), γ (K0III), δ¹ (K0III) and 75 (K2III) are members that have already evolved off the main sequence.

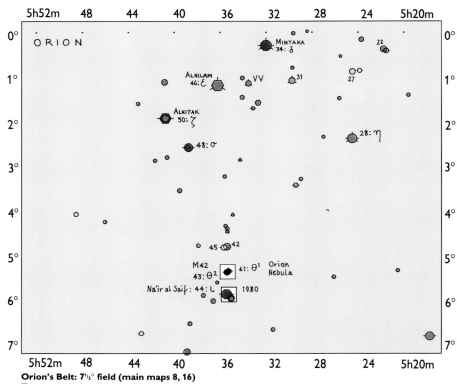

Orion's Belt: 7½° field (main maps 8, 16)
The magnitude limit for seeing colour in blue stars with the naked eye is about m. 1·5, so binoculars are needed to bring out the exquisite colour of the three stars of the belt: δ (O9·5II), ε (B0Ia), and ζ (O9·5Ib + B0III). Visualized with σ, η, and the stars of the sword, this field is sometimes called 'Venus's mirror', because of its resemblance to a hand-held looking-glass.

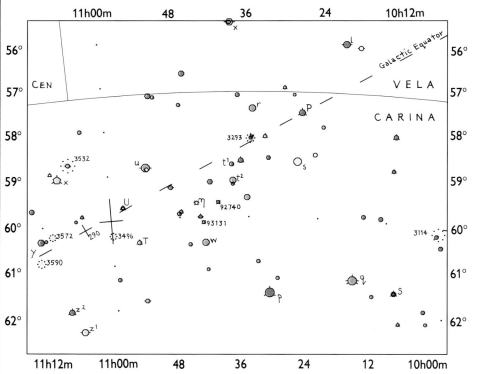

Eta Carinae: 7½° field (main maps 14, 15, 19, 20)
η Carinae is a Pec(e), S Doradus type, m. −0·8 to +7·9. S Doradus variables are typified by irregular light changes, diffuse nebulae, and expanding envelopes; most are B types, but a spectrogram of η Carinae cannot be taken because the star is shrouded in dust (see p. 7). Other stars in the field are 92740, WN7; 93131 WN7; S Car, K5e–M6e, Mira type m. 4·5–9·9, 149 days; T Car, probably not variable; U Car, F6–G7Iab, classical Cepheid, m. 5·7–7·0, 39 days.

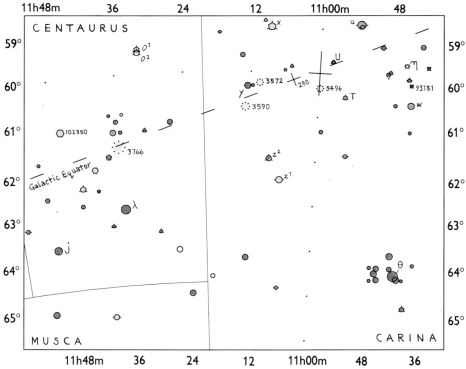

Theta Carinae: 7½° field (main maps 14, 15, 19, 20)
This field is shown in order to separate the cluster of stars around θ Carinae, numbered IC 2606. More interesting as a colour field is the small grouping north of NGC 3766, although a telescope would be required to see colour in stars of this magnitude.

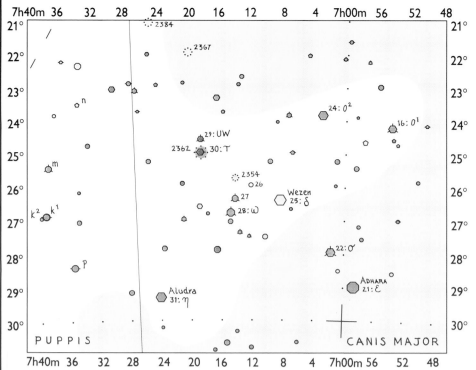

Delta Canis Majoris: 10° field (main map 16)
This field is one of many possible binocular fields showing interesting colour contrasts. 29=UW CMa, O8, is an eclipsing contact system of the Beta Lyrae type, *m.* 4·8–5·3, 4·4 days.

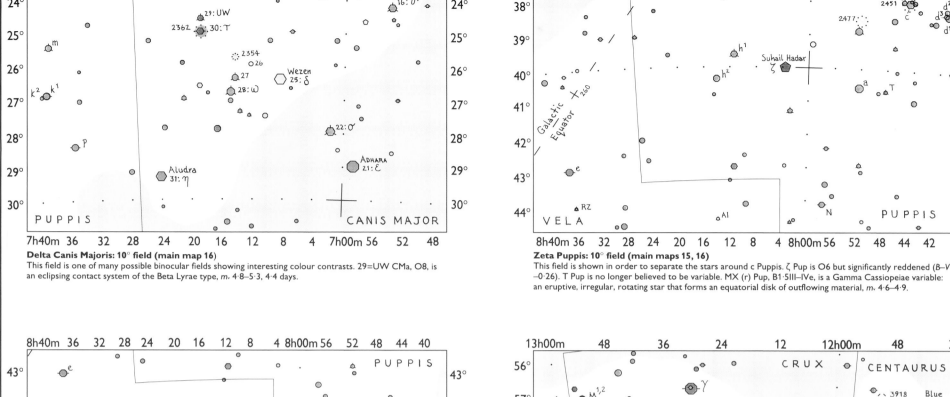

Zeta Puppis: 10° field (main maps 15, 16)
This field is shown in order to separate the stars around c Puppis. ζ Pup is O6 but significantly reddened (B–V −0·26). T Pup is no longer believed to be variable. MX (r) Pup, B1·5III–IVe, is a Gamma Cassiopeiae variable: an eruptive, irregular, rotating star that forms an equatorial disk of outflowing material, *m.* 4·6–4·9.

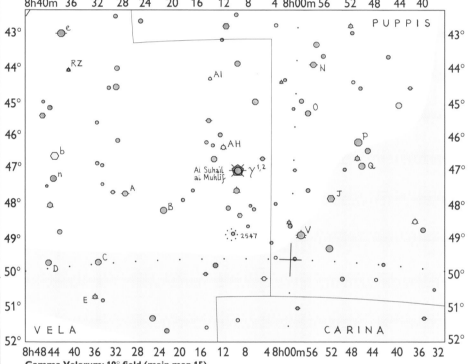

Gamma Velorum: 10° field (main map 15)
γ Vel: WC7 + B3V, separation 41". RZ Vel: G1Ib–G8, classical Cepheid, *m.* 6·4–7·6, 20·4 days. AI Vel: Delta Scuti variable (pulsating), *m.* 6·2–6·8, 0·11 days.

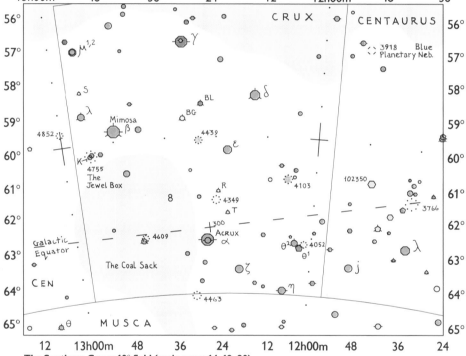

The Southern Cross: 10° field (main maps 14, 19, 20)
β, δ, θ¹, and λ Crucis are all Beta Cephei type, pulsating variables with amplitudes of 0·1–0·3 magnitudes. S, T, R, and BG Crucis are all classical Cepheids, spectra moving from middle to early G at minimum, to early G to late F at maximum, typical amplitudes in the region of 0·7 magnitudes. NGC 4755 is the Jewel Box cluster, resolved in a telescope into 'a collection of glittering coloured stars' (*Norton's 2000.0*).

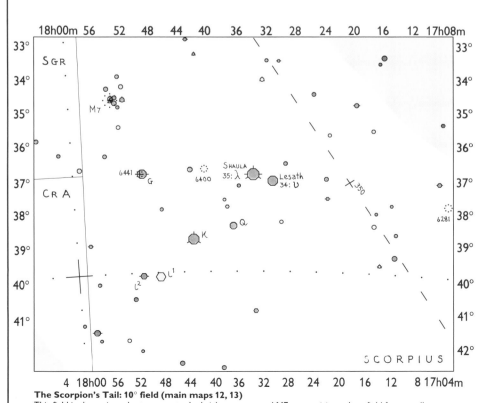

The Scorpion's Tail: 10° field (main maps 12, 13)
This field is shown in order to separate the bright stars around M7, a promising colour field for a small telescope. Unfortunately out of frame is NGC 6231, north of ζ Scorpii, a cluster rich in O types, four of which are brighter than *m.* 6·75, but too close to be resolved on the main map.

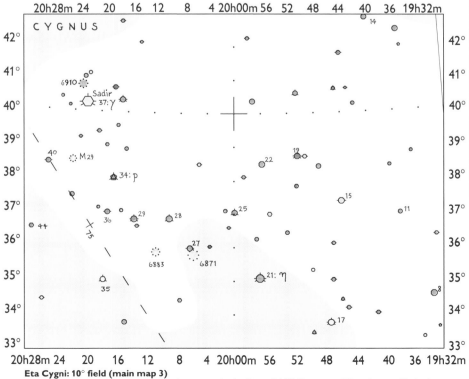

Eta Cygni: 10° field (main map 3)
This field shows a wide range of spectral types north of η Cygni. 34 (P) Cygni is an S Doradus variable (rather more typical than η Car), B1Ia(pec), *m.* 3–6 with no regular period.

Giant Stars

As hydrogen is converted to helium in a star's core, the core contracts and increases in temperature. In stars of more than 0·5 solar masses, the temperature eventually gets high enough to start hydrogen burning in a shell around a core of inert helium. At this point the star moves off the main sequence, heading upwards and to the right on the HR diagram, becoming a *red giant*.

What happens is this: shell burning moves the reaction outwards into fresh supplies of hydrogen in the star's outer regions. This generates a surge of energy release, but it makes the outer layers of the star expand and cool down. A given area of surface is radiating less energy than before, but because the radiating surface is so much larger the overall luminosity becomes hundreds of times greater. After the first surge of shell burning the energy release drops off, and the star moves down the HR diagram, but it still remains among the giants. Eventually the star accumulates at its core enough helium at a sufficiently high temperature for the conversion of helium to carbon to begin.

What the star does next depends on its mass. In a low mass star the onset of helium burning – the *helium flash* – is so sudden that it may never recover. The stellar envelope balloons outwards, cools off, contracts, and fires up again in a series of irregular pulses. With each pulse, some of the atmosphere just keeps on going, and stellar material is lost. Eventually the core runs out of helium, and there is nothing left but a shell of expanding gas briefly illuminated as a *planetary nebula* and a core of inert carbon that contracts, heats up, moves briefly sideways across the HR diagram into the blue end of the spectrum, and then drops down into the realm of the white dwarfs.

In a star of more than 2 solar masses, the onset of helium burning is more gradual, and the star enjoys a second, stable period as a higher luminosity red giant. When core helium is exhausted, higher temperatures produce a helium burning shell inside a hydrogen burning shell. High mass stars can go on to produce core temperatures sufficient to initiate reactions that fuse carbon into neon and magnesium, neon into oxygen and magnesium, oxygen into sulphur and silicon, and sulphur and silicon into iron, all these reactions except the last moving out to take place in a series of concentric shells. Transition into more complicated fuel economies produces instabilities, and while high mass stars enjoy periods as quiet giants (and very high mass stars as quiet supergiants), they also go through phases as variable giants of early spectral class.

Late Stages in Evolution

Whatever the exact course of a star's progress around the HR diagram, the general picture is one of a star progressing upwards and to the right, and in its last stages becoming increasingly unstable and variable, in which condition anything up to 80% of its mass may be lost. What happens in the end depends on how much of its mass remains. Stars of low eventual mass blow off their remaining atmosphere as a planetary nebula.

Once successive fusion reactions have transformed the core of a high mass star into iron, there are no energy-yielding reactions left. The bonding structure of the iron atom's nucleus is the most energy efficient of all the elements; fusing iron atoms into heavier elements is possible, but it does not release energy, it requires it. With no source of energy, cores greater than 1·4 solar masses are believed to collapse, fusing electrons with protons to form neutrons. The remaining envelope crashes inwards after the collapsing core, and then explodes outwards in a chaotic fusion reaction – a *supernova* explosion. The reactions that take place in these explosions are believed to be responsible for the (energy-absorbing) creation of elements heavier than iron. These elements form part of the dust cloud that drifts away from the site of the explosion, enriching the stock of interstellar dust, and eventually forming new stars and planets.

Objects Shown on the Maps

The Milky Way

All the stars that can be seen with the naked eye are part of the same galaxy, the Milky Way Galaxy, of which our Sun is a member. The Milky Way Galaxy contains more than two hundred thousand million stars, most of which are distributed in the shape of a disk about 100,000 light years across and 3,000 light years thick, rising to 12,000 light years at the galactic centre. Away from the centre the luminous material is concentrated in an uncertain number of trailing arms that would make it look, in plan, rather like a Catherine wheel.

The Sun is situated in the arm known as the Cygnus Arm, about 30,000 light years from the galactic centre. The most distant naked-eye stars (stars that can be seen without binoculars or telescope) are about 3,000 light years away, and the Milky Way appears (in dark, clear skies) as a band of light, resolved into individual stars only in binoculars or a telescope. The centre of the galaxy lies beyond the stars that make up the constellation Sagittarius, and is hidden by the clouds of gas and dust that are concentrated in the spiral arms. Most starbirth we observe takes place in these gas clouds, so most of the O and B type stars visible are close to the galactic equator, having formed in the spiral arms.

Multiple Stars

Many stars are part of *multiple systems* in which two or more stars are in orbit around a mutual centre of gravity. Systems of two members (*binaries*) are the most common, but many systems are composed of three or more members. Castor and Pollux, the Twins (Gemini), are good examples of complicated systems. The brightest components of Castor are two main sequence stars, A1 and A3, both of which are themselves binaries; a third binary also belongs to the system, making a total of six. Pollux has one bright member, a giant K type (K0III), and perhaps as many as eight companions.

Unusual Spectral Types

Wolf–Rayet stars (WR stars) are very hot stars (up to 50,000 K) whose spectra are characterized by strong emission lines and weak absorption lines, created by a rapid outflow of stellar material. In many cases this is visible as a gas cloud surrounding the star, but the reason for the loss of material remains unclear.

Stars of late spectral type exhibiting strong carbon and weak oxygen absorption lines are classified R and N in earlier versions of the Harvard system. The sequence R1 to R9 parallels the sequence G4 to K5, and the N sequence runs roughly in parallel with M. Many of these stars have since been reclassified as *carbon stars* (C), giant stars similarly characterized by strong carbon and weak oxygen lines. Some have been classified as carbon rich G, K, and M types, but a few are still classified according to the old system.

S types, similarly carried over from an earlier classification system, are stars whose spectra show molecular bands of zirconium oxide rather than the titanium oxide bands more commonly found in giant M types. S types have mostly been reclassified as carbon stars or M types.

Peculiar stars, designated pec, are stars whose spectrum resists any standard classification.

Variable Stars

Variable stars are of two sorts: extrinsic and intrinsic. Most extrinsic variables are *eclipsing* types, such as Algol, where two or more stars are part of a multiple system whose orbital plane is in line with our line of sight. As one star in the system passes in front of or behind another, the combined apparent magnitude of the system is lowered, producing an observed variability in brightness. About 20% of stars identified as variable are of this eclipsing type.

Intrinsic variables are stars whose variability is a consequence of the inner workings of the star itself. The most common cause of variability is that the forces of gravity (tending to contract the star) and radiation (tending to expand it) are not in balance, but involved in some seesaw effect. Such imbalance is most likely to occur when the star is in transition from, for example, hydrogen to helium burning; on the HR diagram such stars are found moving between different classes of giant.

Another cause of variability is that at some crucial temperature a star's atmosphere can become particularly absorbent of radiation: the atmosphere expands, cools down, becomes transparent, and drops back towards the surface of the star, only to repeat the process. Variability can also originate in the interior of a star powered by more than one fusion reaction taking place in a series of shells: as an inner shell fires up the envelope expands, cooling off the adjacent outer shell to the point where it stops working. The outer shell supplies the inner shell with fuel, so the inner shell eventually stops working as well. The envelope cools down and contracts, the outer shell fires up again, supplying the inner shell with more fuel, and the whole cycle starts again.

About 25% of (identified) intrinsic variable stars are *semi-regular* or *irregular* variables, mostly K and M giants. The remaining 75% can be identified as belonging to particular types, mostly named after a prototype (such as δ Cephei), the first star to be discovered that shows a particular pattern of amplitude (the average difference between its brightness at maximum and minimum, expressed in magnitudes) and period (the average time between maximum and maximum), subsequently identified in other stars of a similar spectral type.

Supernovae

Supernova explosions produce a burst of luminosity that exceeds M_v −15. Such supernovae are rare events. Estimates of how often they occur are controversial: it could be that about three occur in our Galaxy every century, but their likely location in the dust-obscured plane of the Milky Way means that most remain hidden. The most recent nearby supernova to be observed was SN 1987A, which became visible to the naked eye as a m_v +3 object in the Large Magellanic Cloud 170,000 light years away.

What happens after a supernova explosion is also controversial. It is believed that the core of SN 1987A will remain as a *neutron star*. Neutron stars appear as radio *pulsars*, rapidly spinning stars with an intense magnetic field that focuses radio energy into beams that sweep round like the beams of a frenetic lighthouse. Alternative fates for a supernova core are to blow itself up at the time of the explosion, or else to collapse entirely to form a *black hole*, a body so gravitationally intense that electromagnetic radiation of any description is no longer able to escape.

Novae

Nova explosions are very much more common than supernova explosions, and about 25 are estimated to occur in our Galaxy each year. Novae are thought to be produced in multiple systems where a white dwarf is in close orbit around a younger, larger star. The white dwarf strips away the outer layers of its companion and then burns the material off in a thermonuclear explosion, producing a peak luminosity of up to M_v −10. There must be a limit to how often a system can undergo this process, but there are several that apparently repeat the performance every 20 to 100 years, and these are known as *recurrent novae*.

Planetary Nebulae

Planetary nebulae are the gaseous envelopes of low mass stars, blown off towards the end of their lifetime (see p. 34). They are so named because their greenish and disk-like forms were thought to resemble the planet Uranus.

Open Clusters

Open clusters are groupings of 20 to 500 stars in a region 10–60 light years across, recently formed in the same gas cloud and sufficiently young not to have yet drifted apart. Most open clusters are found close to the plane of the Galaxy. Some are still shrouded in gas, and it is likely that star formation is still going on in them. Older groups (such as the Pleiades) show only vestigial wisps of gas, and in still older groups (such as the Hyades) the more massive stars have already evolved off the main sequence. Because stars evolve into giants of later spectral type, it is possible to find the age of such groups by identifying the spectral type of the earliest (and still main sequence) member.

Globular Clusters

Globular clusters are clusters of anything from fifty thousand to a million stars packed into spherical clumps less than 150 light years in diameter. Unlike the rest of the visible Galaxy, globular clusters are not concentrated in the Milky Way, but appear to be orbiting the galactic centre in a spherical halo at a typical distance of 60,000 light years. The earliest spectral types that can be observed in globular clusters are in the region of F2; in some clusters the spectrum is as late as G5. Their spectra are deficient in metal lines, showing that they are subdwarfs (luminosity class VI) formed before the recycling of stellar material in such processes as supernova explosions had properly begun. With no metal content to help convective processes in the interior, subdwarfs burn cooler and slower than their main sequence counterparts, and globular clusters consist of stars perhaps 10 to 12 thousand million years old, formed early in the life of the Galaxy.

Gas Clouds

As well as stars, the Milky Way contains enormous clouds of gas and dust, known as *nebulae*. A typical gas cloud will consist of about 90% hydrogen, 9% helium, and 1% carbon, silicon, oxygen (in silicates), and other 'trace' elements. These gas clouds are mostly observed as dark patches in the sky where the light from more distant stars has been shut off (examples are the Cygnus Rift and the Coalsack), but in some areas the gas has coalesced to form stars (what causes this to happen is not entirely understood). The gas that is left over is driven away by radiation pressure (light and other forms of radiation exert a pressure), but where star formation is recent or is still continuing, the surrounding gas is heated to the point where it begins to radiate its own light; most of the gas clouds shown on the maps are of this type.

Galaxies

Galaxies are 'island universes' of stars, discrete concentrations of tens and hundreds of thousands of millions of stars separated by the enormous distances of near-empty intergalactic space. The two brightest (because nearest) galaxies external to our own Milky Way Galaxy are the Large and Small Magellanic Clouds, *dwarf galaxies* at distances of respectively 170,000 and 200,000 light years, the nearest of ten dwarf galaxy satellites of the Milky Way. The nearest 2·4 million light years) large galaxy is the Andromeda Galaxy, M31, visible to the naked eye as a misty smudge. Like the Milky Way Galaxy, M31 is a spiral galaxy with several attendant dwarf galaxies, and from a distance our own Galaxy would look very much like it.

Galaxies come in a variety of sizes and structures. Some, like the Milky Way and M31, are disk-like *spiral galaxies*. *Elliptical galaxies* show no concentrated bands of material, but range from the egg-like to the spherical. *Irregular galaxies* (such as the irregular dwarf Magellanic Clouds) are just that: irregular in form.

The Maps

The convention for celestial maps is to show stars and other objects as if they lay on the inside of a hollow sphere representing the sky, plotted according to their right ascension and declination. *Right ascension* (RA) is the counterpart of terrestrial longitude and measures how far round the celestial sphere an object is from a zero point in the constellation Pisces. It runs from 0 to 24 hours, corresponding to the apparent daily rotation of the sky. *Declination* (Dec.) is similar to terrestrial latitude, measuring in degrees how far up or down an object is from the celestial equator, from 0° at the equator to 90° at the celestial poles.

The maps in this atlas are computer plotted using data from astronomical catalogues, and annotated by hand. With the exception of the equatorial projections on the centre pages, every map is a polar projection, projected from the centre of the field; in the main maps the centre is at declination $\pm75°$ or $\pm30°$. The $\pm30°$ series appear in order of decreasing right ascension; this is contrary to convention, but ensures that the areas of overlap found in each pair of maps lie next to each other.

Data for star positions have been taken from the Yale *Bright Star Catalogue* (5th edition) and from an updated version of its *Supplement*. The limiting magnitude (that of the faintest stars shown) is $m_v +6·75$. Non-stellar objects (star clusters, gas clouds, and galaxies) have been plotted from the *Revised New General Catalogue of Non-Stellar Objects*. Clusters and gas clouds are shown to a limiting magnitude of $m_v +9·5$; galaxies are shown to $m_v +11·5$. Supplementary data have been taken from sources listed on p. 2.

Stars

The major constellations of the northern and equatorial skies are the classical Graeco-Egyptian groupings, deriving from the Babylonian, that were defined by Ptolemy in about AD 140. Minor constellations were split off in the seventeenth century, and southern constellations were added in the seventeenth and eighteenth centuries. Precise boundaries remained in dispute, and were settled by the International Astronomical Union in 1930. These boundaries (shown on the maps) have had the effect of separating some stars from their parent constellations.

Individual stars are identified in several ways. Proper names are the oldest system, and the oldest of these are Arabic names, often corrupted by transcription and transmission. Many star names have variant spellings, and some stars have gathered more than one name. Where usage has settled on a definitive name it is shown in capital letters; otherwise the name is shown in lower case.

Bayer letters are letters of the Greek alphabet (Table 2), assigned to the stars of a constellation usually so that α (alpha) denotes the brightest star β (beta) the second brightest, and so on. In some cases a Bayer letter is shared among a number of stars by means of superscripted numbers (e.g. δ^1, δ^2). An extension to the Bayer system assigned to the fainter

Table 2 The Greek Alphabet

α Alpha	η Eta	ν Nu	τ Tau
β Beta	θ Theta	ξ Xi	υ Upsilon
γ Gamma	ι Iota	ο Omicron	φ Phi
δ Delta	κ Kappa	π Pi	χ Chi
ε Epsilon	λ Lambda	ρ Rho	ψ Psi
ζ Zeta	μ Mu	σ Sigma	ω Omega

stars of a constellation, if necessary, the lower case roman letters (a, b, c, etc.); if more letters were required the capital letters were also used, as far as Q.

Flamsteed numbers (1, 2, 3, etc.) identify the brighter stars in each constellation, starting from the west. Numbers with one, two, or three digits next to star symbols on the maps are Flamsteed numbers. Where a star has a Bayer designation, the Flamsteed number is not normally shown. Flamsteed numbers do not extend to the southernmost skies.

Argelander codes originally employed the capital roman letters R to Z to denote variable stars by constellation. The system has since been extended to make use of double letters RR to RZ, SS to SZ, and so on to ZZ, then AA to AZ, BB to BZ, as far as QZ (Js are omitted). Beyond QZ (the 334th such designation), the sequence continues with V335, V336, and so on.

To complete the star's designation, the letter or number is followed by the genitive case of the Latin constellation name, or in shortened form by a three-letter abbreviation (see the Index to Constellations on pp. 8–9).

Five- and six-digit numbers are (HD) identifications from the *Henry Draper Catalogue* of 1918–24, a catalogue listing the spectral type of just under a quarter of a million stars.

The colours of star symbols indicate the spectral type (O, B, A, F, G, K, M) or temperature equivalent. They do not represent the colours that can be seen by eye, although they are related; the relationship between spectral type and perceived colour is discussed on p. 38.

Different symbols are used to distinguish luminosity classes:

main sequence star (luminosity class V)

giant star (luminosity class II, III, or IV)

supergiant star (luminosity class I)

A star listed as intermediate between classes I and II or between IV and V is represented by the symbol for the brighter class.

Star of no identified luminosity class

If of early spectral type, these may be stars in a transitional phase of their evolution, off the main sequence. If of late spectral type, they may be variables whose luminosity moves them from one class to another. However, in many cases they are stars whose luminosity class has not been identified or resists identification.

Symbol Flags

These are used in conjunction with any of the symbols shown above, and may also occur in combination.

Multiple star

Where a second star in a multiple system is brighter than $m_v +6·75$ it is also plotted, and if there are no further known members the primary is flagged. Where a second star in a multiple system is shown plotted inside the symbol for the primary, it is sometimes possible to represent the spectral type of only one star, and in these cases it is the spectral type of the primary that is shown. Some ambiguous cases are noted in the keys to particular maps.

Variable star

Variable star showing one magnitude of amplitude or more

Variable star which is also multiple

Unusual or peculiar spectral type (see p. 34)

These are coloured according to the temperature equivalence:

WR as if they were O
R0–R2, C0–C2 as if they were G
R3–R9, C3–C5 as if they were K
N, S, C6–C9 as if they were M

Nova

Identification gives year of observation.

Recurrent nova

Years of observation are listed in the key.

Supernova

Identification gives year of observation.

Non-stellar Objects
Numbers prefixed by a capital roman 'M', M1 to M110, are designations from Charles Messier's catalogues of 1784 and 1786. Numbers of two, three, or four digits shown on the maps next to any of the symbols below are NGC numbers from the *New General Catalogue* originally prepared by J. L. E. Dreyer and published in 1888. Object names (shown in lower case) are popular names in current use.

Many non-stellar objects are diffuse: their light is not concentrated in a single star-like point, but is spread out over a small area of sky. The magnitudes of diffuse objects, however, are reckoned as if all their light did come from a single point. For this reason, the larger the apparent size of the object, the less bright it will appear than is suggested by its magnitude.

In this atlas the limiting magnitude for galaxies is 11·5, and 8·5 for other non-stellar objects. Although these objects are faint, they are of considerable interest to telescope users and astrophotographers.

Planetary nebula

Open cluster

Colour shows the spectral type of the earliest (hottest) member.

Globular cluster

Colour shows composite spectral class.

Gas cloud

Colour assigned according to a comparison of photographic plates; the magnitude is, by convention, that of the illuminating star.

Galaxy

The symbol is purely a convention, and does not imply any representation of appearance or orientation. The colour represents observed *B − V* (see below), which can be affected by orientation; spiral galaxies observed face-on will appear bluer than spiral galaxies observed edge-on.

The outline of the Milky Way is based on photographs. Irregularities in the outline and 'lanes' within the Milky Way represent the presence of foreground dust clouds obscuring the light of the stars beyond.

Colour Index

The *colour index* of a star serves as a measure of its colour, and is found by comparing its magnitude at particular wavelengths. Visual magnitude (in this context denoted by *V*, which is equivalent to m_v – see p. 4) is the standard measure of how bright an object appears to the human eye, and is made over a band of wavelengths centred on 550 nm, in green–yellow

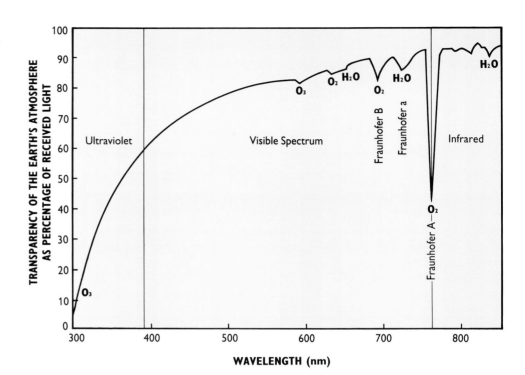

Figure 8 Transparency of the Earth's Atmosphere for Different Wavelengths

The atmosphere is more transparent to red light than to blue, although significant absorptions are made by water vapour and by oxygen at the red end of the spectrum (producing the Franuhofer lines A and B). The Earth's atmosphere has a reddening effect on starlight, most commonly observed in its effects on sunlight.

light. Blue magnitude, *B*, is a measurement of brightness at wavelengths centred at 440 nm, in the indigo–blue. Other measurements are *U* (ultraviolet) at 360 nm, *R* (red) at 700 nm, and *I* (infrared) at 900 nm.

Hot stars, O and B types, radiate more energy at the blue end of the spectrum than at the red end. The colour index *B − V* compares the magnitudes at 440 nm (*B*) and 550 nm (*V*). Because hot stars are brighter at 440 than at 550 nm, when the *V* magnitude is subtracted from the *B* magnitude the result is negative. Cool stars, K and M types, are brighter at the red end than the blue end, so when *V* is subtracted from *B* the result is positive. *B − V* is the principal measurement of star colour, but other readings are also taken: *U − B* gives a measure of ultraviolet radiation, and *I − R* a measure of radiation in the infrared.

The absorption effects in a star's atmosphere determine how much radiation escapes at particular wavelengths. All stars show significant absorption in the ultraviolet, but this does not have a marked effect on perceived colour because the wavelengths are short of visible light. K and M types show the most absorption, but this takes place across the whole visible spectrum, and these stars radiate so much more energy in the red than in the blue that perceived colour is not affected. The best examples of absorption in a star's atmosphere influencing perceived colour are provided by A and F types, for which absorption by hydrogen has the effect of diminishing radiation in the visible blue.

The Earth's atmosphere also absorbs electromagnetic radiation, and is more transparent to red light than to blue (see Fig. 8). About 90% of red light (700 nm) gets through to sea-level, about 80% of green–yellow (550 nm), and only 70% of blue (440 nm). The exact proportion that gets through is affected by the water content of the atmosphere, by dust pollution, and of course by the observer's height above sea-level.

Interstellar dust and gas clouds have a similar absorbing effect, reddening the light from more

distant objects, and this is more marked for objects close to the Milky Way, where dust and gas clouds are concentrated. Reddening by the Earth's atmosphere and by interstellar dust introduces two adjustments that are made in the measurement of colour index.

As observations are made from observatories at different altitudes under varying atmospheric conditions, the recording of *B* and *V* magnitudes is calibrated on a standard star: Vega, α Lyrae. Vega was chosen because it is a bright (m_v +0·03) and stable example of a spectral prototype, A0V, close enough (26 light years) to be unreddened by interstellar dust, and conveniently near the zenith (Dec. +39°) for northern hemisphere observers. Vega was accordingly assigned a *B − V* index of 0·00, and this value is used for the calibration of readings for other objects. However, because Vega is actually rather brighter at blue wavelengths than at yellow–green, a *B − V* of 0·00 describes a blue–white star rather than a true white one. A true equivalence of blue and green–yellow radiation is not reached until a *B − V* of +0·5.

Observed *B − V* describes the colour index of a star (or any other visible object) when observed from the neighbourhood of the Sun, and is adjusted to exclude the reddening effects of the Earth's atmosphere. Intrinsic *B − V* is an assessment of the colour index of the radiation as it leaves the star, and is prepared by analysis of spectral type. The difference between the observed and intrinsic values gives a measure of interstellar reddening, and this difference becomes greater for more distant stars and stars close to the

Figure 9 Spectrum Showing the Peak Sensitivities of the Human Eye

The eye contains four types of light-sensitive cell. Three kinds of cone have peak sensitivities to light at 430 nm (short cones), 530 nm (medium cones), and 560 nm (long cones), and rods have a peak sensitivity to light at 500 nm. Each cell type is sensitive to light over a range of wavelengths, so that the sensitivities of the cell types overlap, embracing an overall range from 390 to 760 nm. Colour perception is by the cones, but colour is seen only when the light source is bright enough to stimulate the cones, and when the image on the retina covers enough individual cells for their response to be compared. Dim light sources stimulate only the rods, and brighter but highly focused images produce small field tritanopia, so the eye tends to perceive the stars as 'White.'

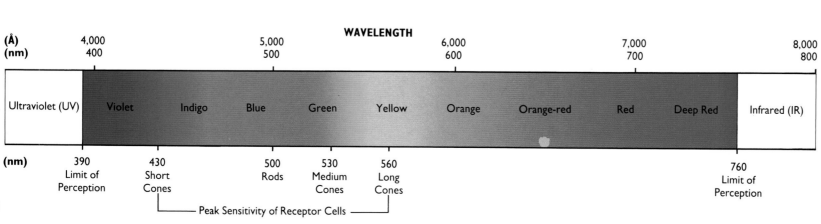

Figure 10 Synthesized Star Colours

The star colours shown here were produced by using an airbrush to blend colours in proportions roughly equivalent to the balance of radiation from particular star types. Spectrum (a) was generated according to blackbody curves. Spectrum (b) mimics the effect of absorption in the Earth's atmosphere combined with the effects of interstellar absorption over 3,000 light years when observed close to the Milky Way. The comparison between these spectra and the colours observed in stars cannot be direct because the reader views these spectra with vision dominated by cones, but would be observing stars with vision dominated by rods.

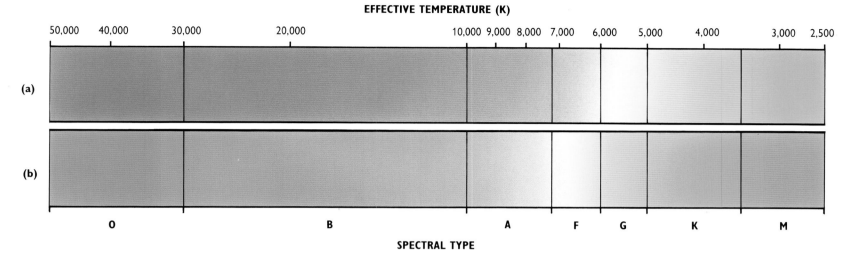

Milky Way. Giant stars of type G onwards are significantly redder than their main sequence counterparts. This is because their outer layers and their atmosphere are so attenuated that they lack the well-defined surface of a main sequence star (the absorption lines that characterize spectral type originate deep within a giant star, not at its visible 'surface').

Colour index and other properties of stars are given in Table 3 for different spectral types and luminosity classes.

The Eye

The light-sensitive cells at the back of the human eye are of two types, *rods* and *cones*. In broad terms it can be said that cones 'see' in colour, and rods 'see' in white, black, and grey. The rods (120,000,000 per eye) greatly outnumber the cones (6,000,000 per eye), although in the *fovea*, a small area of about 0·5 mm diameter at the centre of the retina, there are only cones. The relationship between rods and cones is not well understood, but it is known that cones are not stimulated by very low levels of light, so that night vision takes on the monochromatic, grey-and-white quality associated with rods. At the very limits of perception the central 1·75° of the visual field is effectively blind, since the fovea contains no rods.

In daylight conditions we see with the cones. Rods play some part in daylight vision (they control the dilation of the pupil for one thing), but their full rôle is uncertain. Both rods and cones adapt to increasing darkness, and can become up to 10,000 times more sensitive, but their comparative ranges are staggered. Under dark conditions cones reach their maximum sensitivity after ten minutes. Rods reach maximum sensitivity after half an hour, and in this condition they are 16 times as sensitive as cones. However, at very low levels cone response is no longer translated into colour, and another way of expressing the difference between rods and cones is to say that, at the maximum sensitivity of the eye, monochromatic vision (vision dominated by rods) is about two hundred times as sensitive as colour vision (vision dominated by cones).

Three types of vision use a different balance of rods and cones: daylight vision relies on cones; twilight vision depends partly on the cones and partly on the rods; night vision is dominated by the rods, but the colour-perceiving ability of the cones is activated if the light source is bright enough (see Fig. 9).

The cones are of three types, and look into different sections of the spectrum. Their ranges overlap, and together they can see from about 390 nm at the blue end to about 760 nm at the red, the limit of vision varying with the individual. 'Long (wavelength) cones' show their greatest sensitivity at 560 nm, yellow–green. 'Medium cones' are most sensitive at 530 nm (true green), and 'short cones' at 430 nm (indigo). Short cones do not behave in quite the same way as medium and long cones; they have a strongly chromatic effect, but do not produce the element of 'brightness' found in the reponse of the medium and long cones. There are no blue cones in the fovea, and no rods either, producing an area of insensitivity that becomes apparent when looking at very faint objects, which disappear when held in the centre of the field of vision, and reappear when the gaze is slightly averted. The fovea consists entirely of medium and long cones. Rods show their greatest sensitivity at 500 nm in an area that is effectively blue–green. Daylight colour perception functions by comparing the response of each of the three kinds of cone to a particular wavelength, or mixture of wavelengths, of light. In conditions of half-light the position is complicated by the contribution of the rods.

It cannot be proved that one person's experience of a particular colour is the same as another's, but it seems simpler to assume it may be so. Nevertheless, large numbers of people (mainly men) are colour-blind to the extent of not being able to discriminate between particular colours, and many people (mainly women) see a different intensity of colour with one eye than with the other. Colour difference between the eyes takes the form of one eye seeing 'hotter' than

Table 3 Properties of Stars

Spectral Type	Main Sequence Stars (Luminosity Class V)							Giants (Luminosity Class III)							Supergiants (Luminosity Class I)							Spectral Type
	Absolute Magnitude M_v	Colour Index B–V	Effective Temperature (K)	Mass (Sun = 1)	Diameter (Sun = 1)	Density (g/cm³)	Visual Luminosity (Sun = 1)	Absolute Magnitude M_v	Colour Index B–V	Effective Temperature (K)	Mass (Sun = 1)	Diameter (Sun = 1)	Density (g/cm³)	Visual Luminosity (Sun = 1)	Absolute Magnitude M_v	Colour Index B–V	Effective Temperature (K)	Mass (Sun = 1)	Diameter (Sun = 1)	Density (g/cm³)	Visual Luminosity (Sun = 1)	
O5	-5·8	-0·35	45,000	50	18	0·01	17,500								-6·8	-0·3	40,000	100	30	0·005	45,000	O5
B0	-4·5	-0·3	30,000	18	7	0·07	5,500	-5·0	-0·3	30,000	20	15	0·008	8,500	-6·4	-0·25	28,000	35	25	0·003	30,000	B0
B5	-1·2	-0·15	15,000	6	4	0·15	260	-2·2	-0·15	15,000	7	8	0·02	650	-6·2	-0·1	14,000	25	40	0·000 5	25,000	B5
A0	+0·7	0·0	10,000	3	2·5	0·25	45	+0·0	0·0	10,000	4	5	0·04	85	-6·3	0·0	10,000	16	50	0·000 2	28,000	A0
A5	+2·0	+0·15	8,500	2	1·7	0·55	14	+0·7	+0·1	8,000				45	-6·6	+0·1	8,500	13	60	0·000 08	37,500	A5
F0	+2·6	+0·3	7,250	1·6	1·4	0·8	8	+1·5	+0·25	7,000				20	-6·6	+0·2	7,500	12	70	0·000 05	37,500	F0
F5	+3·4	+0·45	6,500	1·4	1·2	1·1	4	+1·6	+0·4	6,500				20	-6·6	+0·3	7,000	11	85	0·000 02	37,500	F5
G0	+4·4	+0·6	6,000	1·1	1·1	1·2	1·5	+1·1	+0·65	5,750	*1·5*	6	*0·01*	30	-6·4	+0·75	5,500	10	110	*0·000 01*	30,000	G0
G2*	+4·83	+0·63	5,800	1	1	1·4	1															G2*
G5	+5·1	+0·7	5,600	0·9	0·9	1·7	0·8	+0·7	+0·85	5,000	2	10	*0·003*	45	-6·2	+1·0	4,850	13	135	*0·000 007*	25,000	G5
K0	+5·9	+0·85	5,000	0·8	0·85	2·3	0·4	+0·5	+1·1	4,500	2·5	15	*0·001*	55	-6·0	+1·3	4,250	13	200	*0·000 002*	20,000	K0
K5	+7·3	+1·15	4,200	0·7	0·72	2·6	0·1	-0·2	+1·5	3,800	2·5	25	*0·000 2*	100	-5·8	+1·65	3,750	14	400	*0·000 000 3*	18,000	K5
M0	+9·0	+1·4	3,500	0·5	0·6	3·2	0·02	-0·4	+1·6	3,200	3	40	*0·000 05*	125	-5·6	+1·8	3,200	14	500	*0·000 000 15*	15,000	M0
M5	+12·0	+1·65	3,000	0·2	0·3	10	0·002	-0·8	+1·7	2,800				180	-5·6	+2·0	2,800	20	800	*0·000 000 05*	15,000	M5

Values in italics are highly uncertain.   * The Sun is a G2V star.

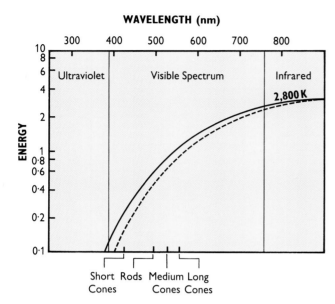

WAVELENGTH (nm)

Figure 11   Blackbody Curve for a Low Temperature Star

Blackbody curve for 2,800 K, equivalent to radiation from a red giant of late spectral type. Red giants display radiation curves (solid line) that rise steeply in the red part of the spectrum, and their red appearance is mildly accentuated by the effects of the Earth's atmosphere (dashed line). (The units of the energy scale are arbitrary.)

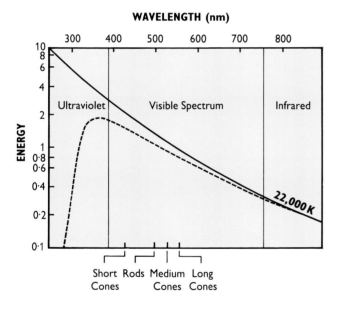

WAVELENGTH (nm)

Figure 12   Blackbody Curve for a High Temperature Star

Blackbody curve for 22,000 K, equivalent to radiation from an early B type. High temperature stars have radiation curves that rise steeply in the blue (solid line). Although the Earth's atmosphere moderates the balance (dashed line), bright B and O types are still plainly blue to the eye. Rather cooler A types appear azure–turquoise to some observers, although others perceive the same stars as 'blue–white', or even 'white'. (The units of the energy scale are arbitrary.)

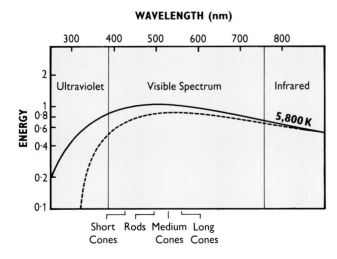

WAVELENGTH (nm)

Figure 13   Blackbody Curve for 5,800 K

Blackbody curve for 5,800 K, equivalent to radiation from the Sun (G2V). When sunlight reaches the Earth's upper atmosphere, its overall colour balance (solid line) is neutral white. By the time the radiation reaches sea-level, atmospheric absorption has shifted the colour balance to yellow–white (dashed line). (The units of the energy scale are arbitrary.)

the other, so that the same colour can appear orange to one eye and yellow to the other. Since a comparison of eyes is added to a comparison of cones, it can be argued that this condition heightens colour discrimination. This would be difficult to prove, but the condition does demonstrate one way in which colour perception can vary among the 'normally' sighted.

In twilight conditions the balance between rods and cones changes in favour of the rods, producing the *Purkinje effect* in which reds become darker, and blues and greens appear lighter than they do by day. Since blue is refracted more strongly than red, the twilight is itself a blue light refracted through the atmosphere from a hidden Sun, so increasing one's sensitivity into the blue is a good way of making the most of twilight. There is an ambiguity in the way rods combine with cones in twilight vision: on the one hand it can be argued that the rods see all light as 'white', and add intensity to things that the cones continue to see as blue or green; on the other hand the effect is to alter the balance of colour, so that there is a sense in which rods are implicated in colour perception.

Two further factors are relevant to the discussion of seeing colour in stars. The first is colour contrast, so that turquoise will appear green in contrast to blue, and blue in contrast to green. Similarly, the eye will perceive an uncontrasted near-white as true white: anyone who has ever put a new coat of white paint onto an old one will have noticed how the old surface suddenly takes on colour by contrast. The second factor is the way the eye sees small bright colour sources as tending to white. In their book *Colours of the Stars*, Malin and Murdin indentify this tendency as 'small field tritanopia', and quote research indicating that yellow and blue are lost before red and green.

Perceiving Colour in Stars

Only the brightest and more strongly coloured stars appear coloured to the naked eye. Binoculars and telescopes increase the amount of light reaching the eye, and this allows colour to be seen in a greater number of stars, including stars of a more subtle colour. The perception of colour is heightened by contrast (subtle colours emerging by comparison with other stars in the same field of view) and by slight defocusing of the instrument (see Figs. 15 to 17 on pp. 39–40), so as to avoid the effects of small field tritanopia.

Colour is most easily seen in giant M and K types (see Fig. 11). The blackbody curves of these stars rise sharply at the red end of the spectrum, so that the star may be radiating ten times as much visible light at the red limit of the eye's sensitivity range than it is in the centre, at 550 nm, where visual magnitude is measured: the blue component of the radiation is low, and the perception of colour is not confused by the 'white' response of the rods. Arcturus (K2IIIp), Aldebaran (K5III), Betelgeuse (M2Ib), and Antares (M1Ib) are all stars that appear orange to red. Just how red they appear depends, among other things, on how close they are to the horizon. When stars are near the horizon their light passes through more of the Earth's atmosphere, increasing the effects of absorption by the atmosphere, which absorbs blue light more strongly than red.

Seeing colour in blue stars (see Fig. 12) is more difficult because colour perception is confused by the white response of the rods. However, Spica (B1V), Regulus (B7V), and Rigel (B8Iae) are all plainly blue to

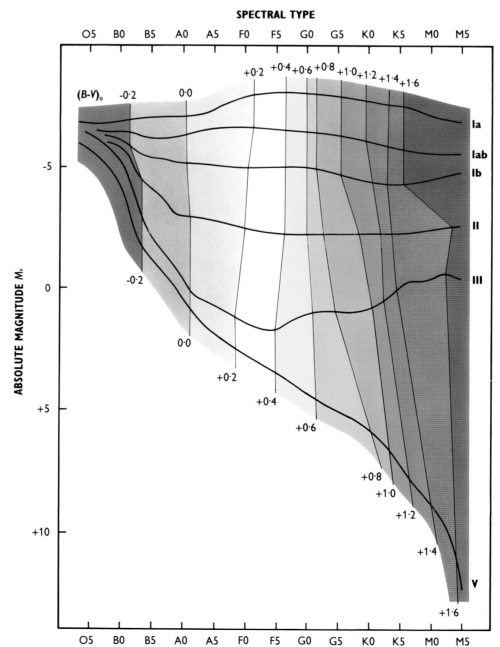

SPECTRAL TYPE

**Figure 14
Variation of *B* — *V* with Luminosity Class**

B — *V* is a standard measure of colour over the range 440–550 nm, which is just within that area of the visible spectrum to which the human eye is most sensitive. Giant G and K types are markedly 'redder' than their dwarf counterparts.

the naked eye. The three stars of Orion's belt, Alnilam (B0Ia), Alnitak (O9·5Ib), and Mintaka (O9·5II), all have a luminosity peak that is well into the ultraviolet, quite unlike anything the eye encounters in everyday life. To the naked eye these stars are just below the magnitude level required to see colour in blue stars (this appears to be around $m_v +1·5$), but when their light is amplified through binoculars or a telescope, they appear as a fine lavender to violet.

A blue–green component is also visible to the naked eye in early A types such as Vega (A0V) and Sirius (A1V), and this raises a controversy: are these stars green? Many astronomers are uncomfortable with the suggestion of green stars, possibly because they consider star colour as deriving from a two-dimensional measure of blue against red. However, the perception of colour in stars is based on four measures (three cones and a rod); research on small field tritanopia indicates that green is more easily seen in small light sources than is blue; and if you ask an inexperienced observer ''What colour is that star?'' and point to Vega, the answer is as often ''Green'' as it is ''Blue''. The seven classes of the Harvard system contain three categories of blue stars: O stars are true violet, B stars are blue, and A stars are towards the centre of the spectrum where blue shades into green, through ambiguous shades of turquoise–azure that are seen as blue by one person, and green by another.

Stars that show more or less flat blackbody curves across the middle of the spectrum are usually perceived as white (see Fig. 13). The Sun is an early G type (G2V), and we are commonly undecided as to whether sunlight is yellow or white. This difficulty is perfectly real: the radiation curve of the Sun is tilted towards the blue–green as it enters the atmosphere, but atmospheric absorption has the effect of tilting it towards the yellow–green by the time it reaches sea-level, with some of the 'missing' blue light scattered by the atmosphere. The result of atmospheric absorption is a blue sky, white light under light cloud, and a yellow–white tone to direct sunlight (*Do not look at the Sun directly! Looking at the Sun damages the eyes, and looking at it through binoculars or a small telescope is enough to cause permanent blindness.*) That the blackbody radiation of a G2 star peaks in the middle (500 nm) of the visible spectrum is hardly a coincidence: the eye has sensibly evolved its peak sensitivity to coincide with the peak luminosity of its local star. Any smooth and roughly equal mix of radiation around the middle of the visible spectrum is perceived as 'white'.

Late A, all F, and early G types have more or less flat blackbody curves through the middle of the spectrum, and all appear more or less white. Just where colour appears in borderline cases, how late among A types and how early among G types, depends on the sensitivity of the observer, and (in binocular and telescopic observation) on the presence of colour contrasted stars in the same field of view. Capella (G8III) looks distinctly yellow to the naked-eye observer, but this is a special case because giant stars of late spectral type are redder than their dwarf counterparts, and because Capella is bright enough to be observed under incompletely dark conditions, when the rod response is muted. An interesting test would be the double star Rigil Kentaurus, G2V + K1V. A more difficult test would be Altair (A7IV–V), which in principle could have a turquoise tinge, but which in practice appears to be white. Figure 14 shows how colour index varies with luminosity class.

One of the fascinations of observing colour in stars is the way colour changes over the period of twilight, over the period of dark-adaption by the eye, and from one night to the next. The planets make interesting contrast effects. For example, Jupiter appears yellow under steady conditions, but observed close to the horizon can appear a brilliant white. Colour is in any case difficult to fix close to the horizon, and rain-washed skies produce wonderful scintillations that defy any attempt to fix true colour. Although

colour is impaired in the light-polluted skies over cities, it can still be seen, and identifying a single bright star on grounds of colour is a satisfying thing to do. Colour is particularly useful in identifying stars briefly revealed on a dark night of racing cloud, times when it is rather wonderful to be outside, but when there is very little else that can be done in the way of observation.

Binoculars and telescopes have the effect of stabilizing colour, which can be further explored by slight defocusing of the equipment (see Figs. 15 to 17) and by slightly averting one's gaze, moving the image in and out of the fovea. Just playing about in this way makes the eye more sensitive, and colour quickly becomes a useful way of navigating among the brighter stars of an unfamiliar field. This is one way in which it is hoped this atlas will benefit the practising observer.

The Anglo-Australian Telescope Board, photography by David Malin.

The Anglo-Australian Telescope Board, photography by David Malin.

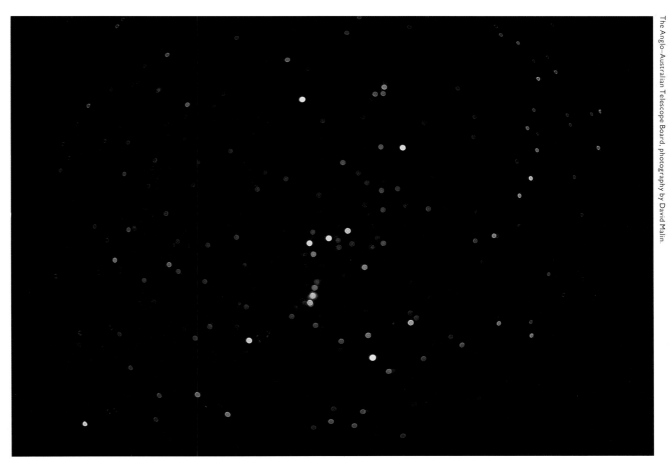

Figure 15 (*top*) Star Colours Recorded by Photography

The Orion star field, photographed with a large format camera tracked in company with the stars. Star colour recorded in photographs works in a reverse way to star colour seen by eye. In colour photographs the colour of the brighter stars is 'burnt out', so bright stars are recorded as white and only the fainter stars are recorded as coloured. The human eye sees only the brightest stars as coloured, all other visible stars appearing white.

Figure 16 (*bottom*) Star Colours Recorded by Defocusing

This photograph shows the same star field as in Fig. 15, but the camera lens has been moved out of focus, spreading the light from individual stars and allowing the film to record more colour. This technique reproduces some of the effects of observing through defocused binoculars and telescopes, where the large, out-of-focus star images assist in the perception of colour (see p. 38).

Figure 17
Star Colours Recorded by Star Trailing in Progressive Defocus

This photograph again shows the Orion star field pictured in Figs. 15 and 16, but here the camera has been kept stationary. The movement of the Earth produces star trails, and progressive defocusing converts these into sectored cones of colour, allowing the effects of different intensities of exposure to be compared. The lavender-blues seen in the trails of the three stars in Orion's belt make an interesting comparison with what can be seen in binoculars. Note also the near-brown colours in the trail of Betelgeuse.

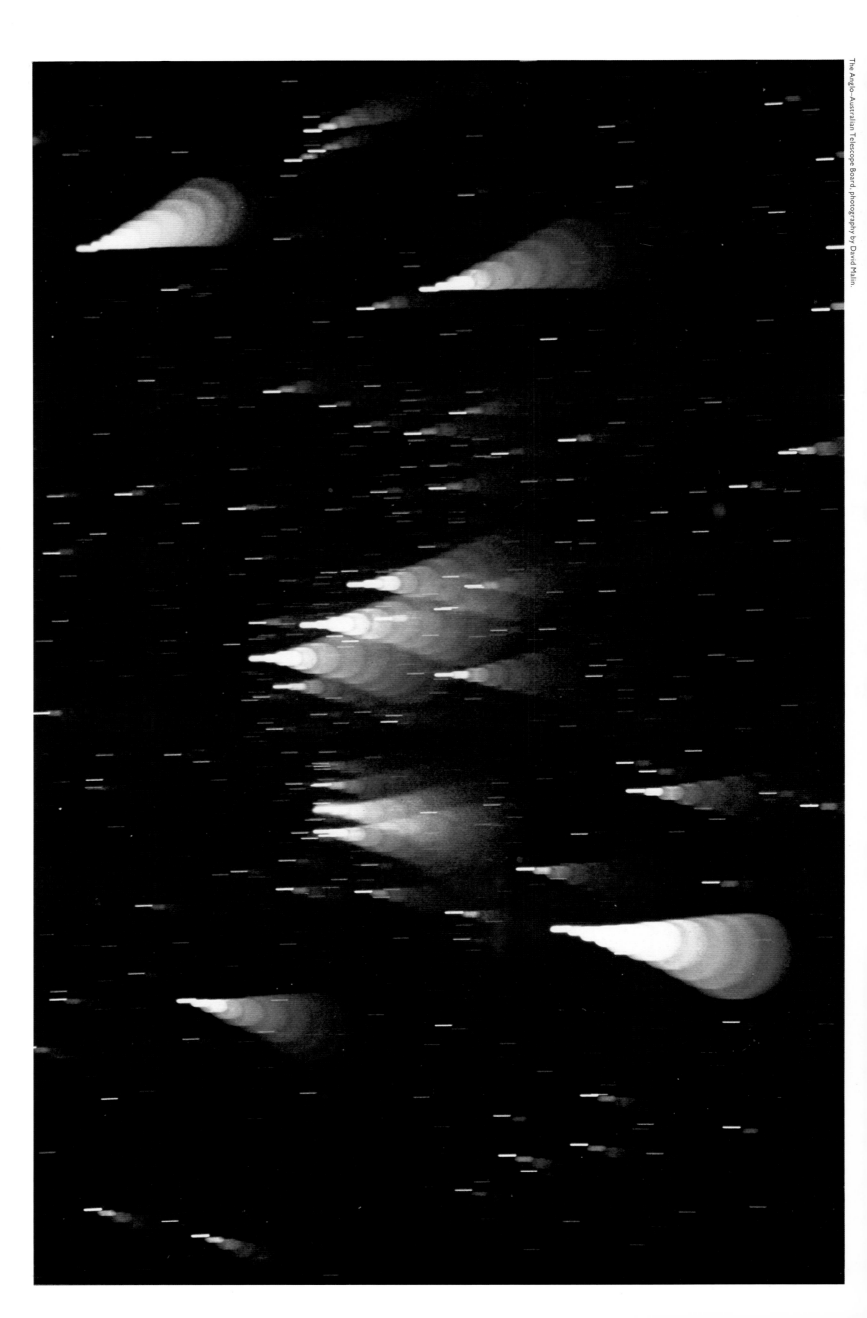

The Anglo-Australian Telescope Board, photography by David Malin.